MW00587835

Rie Frilund Skårhøj

MEDITATIVE MOVEMENTS

CHRIST CENTERED YOGA WITH DEVOTIONAL PRAYER

Prayers written by : Dorte Kappelgaard
Translation Editor : Yvonne Miloyevich

Re:Source

Author Rie Frilund Skårhøj
The prayers are written Dorte Kappelgaard
Translation Editor: Yvonne Miloyevich
Also: Christina Villadsen, Pernille, Kalith,
Linda, Berit, Ragna, Anne Julia

Published by Re:Source
Copenhagen 2019

Copyright © by Rie Frilund Skårhøj.
All rights reserved.
Send an email if you want to use part of the
book for free: rie@crossyoga.org

Pictures: Rie Frilund Skårhøj
Models: Rie Frilund Skårhøj
and Louise Rostgaard
Design: By Judith ApS
ISBN: 978-87-970998-1-0

THANK YOU

I want to thank Yvonne for spending hours proof reading this book and giving feedback. It's a blessing to know you!

Dorte Kappelgaard has written the beautiful prayers in the book. Dorte you have a unique gift of expressing yourself poetically. Thank you.

Thank you Louise Rostgaard, who is featured as the other 'model' in the photos. I enjoy our friendship tremendously.

Thank you, all of my friends, who have offered their feedback in the initial stages of this book. That has been very valuable! Thank you all instructors in Cross Yoga for the encouragement in the development phase of the book.

Thank you Judith Jønsby for the beautiful layout. It has been a pleasure to cooperate with you!

Thank you my dear family. My Mom and Dad, who have shown me how precious and valuable faith is. Thank you my wonderful children Amelie, Noomi and Tristan, who are putting up with a mother who has wild ideas, and who loves to travel. My life would be empty without you. Thank you my husband Kasper for your big support of this book project and CrossYoga in Europe. Thank you for believing in me and encouraging me to live out my dreams.

The greatest THANK YOU goes out to God. I am so grateful for life and grace that you have provided through Jesus Christ. Your love for me does not depend on my capabilities or on anything I can accomplish. You love me just as I am. THAT is the foundation and the drive in my life.

TABLE OF CONTENTS

INTRODUCTION 6

How Do I Get Started? 6

Is It Really Worth It? 10

CHRISTIAN MEDITATION - A BRIEF INTRODUCTION ...18

Christian Meditation In This Book - How To? 20

HOW TO USE THE BOOK 22

You Might Also Like To Know 25

Movement Is Healthy If You Listen To Your Body 26

THE DEVOTIONS 29

The Love Of God And Meaning Of Love 30

Peace 38

Surrender 46

When You Are Longing And Searching For God 54

Trust 64

Faith 72

If You Are Tired And Long For Rest 80

When You Experience Fear Or Worry 88

Worship God 96

When You Are Frustrated 104

When You Want To Pray For Others 112

When You Don't Have Words 118

When You Are Sad 126

Grateful 134

When You Lack Energy And Courage...................................142

MOVEMENTS AND ROUTINES 151

ABOUT THE AUTHOR RIE FRILUND SKÅRHØJ 178

BIBLIOGRAPHY 180

INTRODUCTION

I have never heard of anyone who was good at meditation from day one. On the other hand I know a great many, who are very impatient, and who conclude after the third try, that they are no good at meditation. This I completely understand. I find it hard to find the time to meditate and I don't have the patience for long meditations! My thoughts wander from one subject to the next, when I attempt to quiet my thoughts. My reason for writing this book is that I have found a set of tools to help me release stress, to quiet my ever-wandering thoughts a bit, and to open my heart to the love and grace of God.

I have experienced that when I combine calm movements and meditation, something unique happens. It becomes easier to focus my thoughts and find peace after calm and slow movements, which do not only have the aim of mere physical performance. It then becomes easier to open up to the joys of meditating. Later in this chapter I will explain why slow movements have a calming effect on the soul and mind. These movements also have the advantage that they take us 'from our head to our body.' Not only do calm movements help still wandering thoughts, but we then include our body in our faith and spiritual journey. This is an holistic approach to Christianity, where through our body, soul and intellect (mind) we receive the love of God.

HOW DO I GET STARTED?

The answer to that question is simple. You start by using this book. Every devotion and meditation in this book is made up of five elements: a prayer, a sequence of movements (whatever sequence you choose from the back of the book), a scripture, a pause called an 'Interlude' which includes various creative or meditative elements, and a final meditation on a short sentence from the Bible. You can mix them up or leave out parts as you like.

There is a huge variety of meditations from which one can choose. This book uses different methods but all chapters have a 'mantra' meditation, which means meditating on the word of God as you repeat a sentence.

The movements you are encouraged to make are pictured in the back of the book. There are three levels of difficulty, so you are free to use whichever movements or routines, you please.

The idea with the routines is to do them slowly, and in a pace aligned with the rhythm of your breathing. You can find all the routines as PDF files at www.crossyoga.org.

Perhaps in time new meditations and movements will be found online – if readers show an interest in them.

Besides the grace of God, most things in life do not come freely and without effort. Slow movements and meditations are like training muscles you probably seldom use. It takes a bit of time and patience but it's not as hard as you might think. Two things, of which many of us do not possess enough. This will be a challenge for most, when they start out with the movements in combination with the meditations in this book. Let us approach one challenge at a time. Here is some good advice available for all the challenges you might experience.

Challenges you will probably face:
- I find it hard to concentrate when I meditate, even though I have tried several times.
- The movements are difficult to do precisely, as they appear in the photos.
- It is a challenge to align my breathing rhythm and the movements.
- Some days it is harder than others to focus on the meditation.

Do not give up. You are not the only one facing these challenges.

IT IS HARD TO CONCENTRATE WHEN I MEDITATE

The brain is an idea machine. It is constantly decoding the present in the light of previous experiences, and the thought of what might happen next. But if your brain was not at work, you might be alive, but be brain-dead. Your brain is very active, even when you sleep.

This means, that when you consciously try to focus your brain activity on one thing only, you are challenging your own brain. The brain simply is not used to focusing only on something simple over longer periods of time. Furthermore, we live in an online era, where we are used to constantly shifting our focus. We have trained our attention to move rapidly from one subject to the next – and typically without much contemplation. We practice daily shifting our thoughts back and forth at a rapid rate from things we have to remember tomorrow, to general worries or personal problems. For example, while in meditation, we suddenly might become aware of the fact, that we are no longer meditating. Instead, we are thinking about the laundry, or an assignment, or we might be trying to interpret someone's behavior. When you experience this, there are two important things to remember:

1. Avoid becoming so annoyed or frustrated that you can't concentrate. These feelings will disturb your meditation even more. Calmly accept that thoughts are free to come and go. Just accept that this is part of the process. You will find that in time it becomes easier to keep focus.

2. Practice letting go of the irrelevant thoughts, just like you would physically let go of a balloon with helium. Avoid lingering on the thoughts which may appear. Your 'to do' list and your problems will still be there after your meditation. You will not find better solutions by constantly brooding over them. For those new to meditation it is a task in itself just to become aware that you are even doing all this thinking about something else. Sometimes, I have been out of my meditation and well into my everyday thoughts for several minutes, before even realizing that my mind was somewhere else.

If you are new to meditation, then start meditating on the Bible verse for only about five minutes. After some time, you can extend your meditations. You can meditate just once or twice a week, and still benefit from it, in my experience. Unfortunately, more time does not seem to come flying at us magically. So if you want to learn to meditate and use the movements, it will only happen if you take time out to do it. Write it in your schedule and set an alarm, so you can help yourself take this time out. For example, it could be twice a week for 20 minutes.

Most books on meditation recommend that you meditate twice a day for 30 minutes. Honestly, I don't want to prioritize an hour every day to meditate. So less will have to do. Will I miss some of the joys and benefits of meditation that an hour would provide? Probably, but I don't feel a calling from God to spend an hour in meditation.

THE MOVEMENTS ARE DIFFICULT TO DO PRECISELY AS SEEN IN THE PICTURES

The photos are meant as a source of inspiration. If you don't feel like moving, then don't. If you choose to move, let the movements be YOURS, and let them be calm and free of performance perfection. This is important! Do not do anything, which will strain your body, just because the photo shows a stretch with a very bowed head or a wide stretch of leg! Let the photos guide you in the direction that is right for your body movements and capabilities. Listen to your body while looking at the photos, and find your own version or alternative. Perhaps you have some books or blocks you can use as 'extensions' for your arms to reach the floor, if your fingers can't and the photo shows hands on the floor.

If you repeat the movements for a couple of weeks, you will experience that you have become stronger and more flexible. Your body will benefit from the stretches and strengthening poses you practice. So I encourage you to be patient when it comes to the movements. At the end of this chapter, you can read more about how you can take care of your body.

IT IS A CHALLENGE TO ALIGN MY BREATHING RHYTHM AND THE MOVEMENTS

This part will fall into place in time. Your breathing should be as natural as possible, and will align physiologically and naturally with the movements, in time. So typically, you will breathe in when you open up your chest by leaning back. You breathe out naturally when you scrunch your body. This is the best way to align your breathing and movements. But it may still feel strange to you, and just be something you need to get used to. Hang in there, and keep trying the same sequence until you feel you have a good rhythm.

Let me emphasize, should you desire to linger in one position longer and draw more breaths you may, if it feels natural. Allow your movements and your breathing to align naturally. Try not to feel you must perform them in a certain way! Sometimes you might feel like aligning calm movement with your breathing, and other days you might want to linger in one position longer. The point is to focus on your body and breathing and not let the need for perfection control you.

SOME DAYS IT IS HARDER TO FOCUS ON THE MEDITATION THAN OTHERS

This is completely natural. Stressful days often cause us to need more time to 'calm down' and find inner peace. Furthermore, hormones and emotions are also reasons for this. The best gift you can give yourself is to accept that maybe today, it is not quite as easy as yesterday. Remind yourself that time with God is never wasted – no matter your perception of how well it is going. Perhaps the present day's scripture or your meditation will make perfect sense in your life tomorrow or next week.

IS IT REALLY WORTH IT?

YES. But it is quite legitimate to question whether meditation and movement, as personal devotion, are for everyone. Perhaps not. But I do believe that a great many people are longing to use physical movement in their spiritual lives. There are numerous reasons why it is also a good idea. In the following chapter, I will discuss the physiological and spiritual explanation models.

The physiological explanation models help us understand why this book makes sense and how we can improve the quality of our lives using movement and meditation. Whereas, the spiritual explanation model helps us use the tools of movement, breathing and meditation as worship and surrender while avoiding 'navel gazing.' It explains why using your body can be a powerful way of expressing your prayer or longing for God.

THE PHYSIOLOGICAL EXPLANATION MODELS

There are endless explanation models which can be used in this context. However, we will work in this book with the cohesion between the body and the brain, as well as various methods of learning and health.

BODY AND BRAIN

Planning, analyzing, thinking of shopping lists, worrying about the future, etc. are activities that put the brain to work. Too many demands and feelings of not being up to the task cause stress reactions in the body. This results, among other things, in the release of the stress hormone cortisol. Cortisol is useful in our bodies short term – as is the case with adrenaline. These hormones give us extra energy to do tasks before a deadline, for example. It is a good thing, so we can perform better, when we need to, short term. However – if we build up stress hormones, because we need peak performance on a daily basis, this can wear out the body and mind. Our bodies are not created to be in constant stress mode.

It is important to mention in this context, that parenting also can be a significant stress factor. We need to raise our children, but not control them. Having children takes up time and can 'disturb' us, even when we need some quiet time or sleep. You may feel 'bad' about feeling annoyed or stressed out by your beloved children. Perhaps you are familiar with the thought: 'I ought to have more energy around my children.' Take a guess at what this thought gives you. Yes – even more stress and feelings of inadequacy.

If you do not address continuous stress caused by work and other life factors, it can cause an uneasy feeling in your body, excessive and overwhelming thoughts, insomnia, anxiety, palpitations, etc. All of which are stress-related symptoms, with which I am sure you are familiar. The body reacts to stress with these physical symptoms, when we have neglected the signals to calm down, which our body sends us. What happens is that the front part of our brain (prefrontal cortex) which controls the impulses from our body is given too much control. Our will power, extreme discipline and sense of duty get the better of us, until our body gives in, because we are not listening to its 'voice.' Our will power in the prefrontal cortex, our consciousness, chooses not to hear our body's natural impulses saying STOP. Therefore we wear our body down.

To most people, who end up on sick leave caused by stress, it comes as a complete surprise when the body gives in to the symptoms. Oftentimes, people will admit to knowing something was wrong, but that they had no idea how bad it was. Or they thought that they would make it through. By focusing on the body's senses and listening to the body's signals, we can bring ourselves from 'brain to body.' We can learn to listen and respect what our body is telling us, and stop listening to our will power, sense of duty, feelings of guilt, and/or need for perfection.

> *Mark 12:31 NRSV*
> *'The second (commandment) is this, 'You shall love your neighbor as yourself.' There is no other commandment greater than these.'*

I believe that 'to love God, your neighbor and yourself' also means to respect your body's signals to you, because if you don't, you basically hurt yourself and others as you wear yourself out. I believe that Jesus tells us to listen to our bodies because it is a way of showing love to God, others and ourselves.
Calm movements can bring us from duty and will power 'down into our body,' because we allow ourselves to activate our senses. By moving slowly and breathing deeply, we become aware of the body. We simply force the brain out of excessive thinking, and give it a break when we focus on our senses, our movements and our breathing. Listening to music when moving also can be a wonderful thing – depending on your preference. When we move free of physical performance between 5 and 20 minutes, for instance, we will experience that our brain to some extent lets go of its 'business.' Perhaps some days it might take longer than other days.

Calming 'excessive' thinking (the 'monkey brain'), and that 'uneasy' feeling in the body is necessary to us, before we can be calm enough to concentrate while meditating. This is why the movements come before the meditations in this book. It is vital, that the movements are calm and not overly strenuous, if we want to achieve that peaceful effect. You might get warmed up by practicing the movements. You may find some positions challenging. Just do not push yourself to the edge of your limit. Your main focus is not 'working out' as you move. A power fitness class will not lower your level of stress – on the contrary, it may do the opposite.

Movements to help contemplation and meditation have the following in common:
- Are slowly performed, at your own pace.
- Are free of performance. This means you should not focus solely on becoming better at doing them.
- Are imperfect. Give your inner perfectionist a break and enjoy moving your body in a way that feels good.
- Are not performed in such a way that you lose your breath. It's not a cardio exercise we do. It is important, that you breathe deeply, as this stimulates the calming parasympathetic nervous system.

The deep breathing, presented in this book, will affect the parasympathetic nervous system. And this will quickly lower the stress hormones in your body. This is the reason we often say 'take a deep breath,' when we encounter unpleasantries or get angry. We calm ourselves when breathing deeply.

One of the reasons for the success of yoga these days is to be found in the constant reminder to breathe deeply – even in difficult physical positions. By practicing our ability to breathe deeply even when we are being physically challenged, we become more robust in our everyday lives. This 'technique' is adaptable to our everyday lives so that we can help ourselves in difficult and/or stressful situations by deep breathing. This gives us improved quality of life.

DIFFERENT METHODS OF LEARNING

Besides the physical explanations of the cohesion of the body and the brain, there is another reason why this devotional book might be an answer to prayers for some. As you might know humans take in knowledge in vastly different ways. The tradition of the Church in general is to value the intellectual over the physical regarding the practice of the faith. Sermons speak to the brain, and we use our hearing and sometimes our sight as primary tools of communication. This leaves us with a one-sided form of learning. For some of us, movement and visualization along with a scripture will allow us to store the essence of the content better in our brains. We adopt knowledge and simply put to better use what we know, when we receive the message through the body in a physical sense. This means that for some people, Christianity makes sense and is applicable when they read scripture or listen to a sermon, while others have to experience it through the body. Others might even have to try it out in the company of others, as they are relational learners. My hope for this book of devotions is that the faith in Jesus Christ will be anchored more deeply within those who learn by involving the body in the process.

HEALTH

One last physiological reason to use movement in devotional practice is that it is healthy. God has given us a fantastic body. It is quite unique and complex. Even the brightest scientists have yet to understand all the complexities of the body, and the link between body and mind. In modern society we often do not use our body the way it was intended. Repetitive movements and/or sitting still at work for long periods of time is hard on the back, shoulders and legs. Our bodies start to hurt, and this affects our everyday lives, and our level of energy. These pains also can keep us from helping others around us. However, if we do lead a somewhat healthy life, stretch out and use our muscles on a regular basis, it will most likely cause greater well-being and energy for ourselves, and those around us. I personally love that I can do something physical and healthy at the same time that I spend time with God. What's not to like? :-)

THE SPIRITUAL OR MENTAL EXPLANATORY MODELS

The spiritual or mental explanatory models are just as important as the physiological. We need a Christian spirituality to embrace us as whole human beings – flaws and all.

WHO YOU ARE, AND WHO GOD IS

When movements and the Bible are used for meditation, we are reminded who God is, and who we are. We bring ourselves from everyday tasks and the business of daily living, 'down into our bodies.' When we are short of time or feel stressed, it is often because we tend to believe that we ourselves play the essential role in 'making everything happen.' We don't listen to the body when it says 'stop' but keep going because we feel we have to. We are afraid of what might happen if we don't 'make' it.

We might believe that our financial security is at risk, or that others find us inadequate, if we do not meet deadlines or standards we have set for ourselves. We might believe that the acceptance of others depends on whether we succeed or not.

This is indeed a false self image. We exalt ourselves to god-level, if we believe that the fallout of circumstances depends on our efforts alone. It is God, who is in control, and God who rules the universe. Our surroundings and our lives do not fall apart, if we do not succeed in accomplishing everything on our endless 'to do' lists! Self-esteem is not to be found in whether or not we are a success in the eyes of the world.

When I say in The Lord's Prayer: 'Your will be done,' then I have to believe that this is exactly what is going to happen. Even if it happens in a different way than I thought it would. I will propose that it is easier for God to show compassion for us, when we let go of our tendency to control and plan, and just trust in God's timing.

I'm not saying that we should do nothing and just wait for things to happen. I'm saying that when we breathe deeply and try our best, trusting that God's schedule or timing is different from ours, we will find peace. My worth does not depend on my achievements, and whether or not I am perfect. God works in mysterious ways. The imperfect work we sometimes feel we do, may be just perfect in the eyes of others. If we want to follow God's plan, attuned to God's peace, we must seek the timing and ambitions God has for us, and not our own.

FROM THE HEAD TO THE HEART

Calm movements and Christian meditations also remind us that we are loved, and that God has compassion for us. In many religions the gods are feared. Humans have to satisfy them by bringing offerings, or they have to do things the 'right' way, to be saved and/or to achieve true wisdom. The God of Christianity tells us to call him 'Father' (feel free to use 'Mother' if the concept of father is not positive for you.) In the Bible we read that God LOVES you and me. Not in some abstract way, but quite literally. If you grew up in a Christian setting, you will probably have heard many times, that God loves you. You also may have heard, and you understand that Jesus died for your sins.

You may understand and believe the logic in the Christian thinking. But do you trust in it? Do you really have faith in it? Do you have a sense (not just a feeling) of the truth of it – in your heart? Enough to build your life upon? Understanding faith and having faith in something are two quite different things.

Movement and meditation help us to perceive and receive the love of God through our hearts and not our heads. Meditation in this context is not just a well articulated theological prayer. A prayer (as we understand it in many churches) calls for conscious thought. Prayer demands that we think in the past tense (e.g., 'Forgive me for having shouted this morning.') It also asks us to think in future narratives (e.g., 'I pray for the day of tomorrow.') It requires us to bring our worries to God (e.g., 'I pray for my friend, who is ill.') Let me just say – there is NOTHING wrong with a very concrete and articulate prayer. By all means, let us all pray more. However, the wordless physical prayer is also very precious.

> *Paul says in Romans 8:26-27 NRSV*
> *Likewise the Spirit helps us in our weakness; for we do not know how to pray as we ought, but that very Spirit intercedes with sighs too deep for words. And God, who searches the heart, knows what is the mind of the Spirit, because the Spirit intercedes for the saints according to the will of God.*

'Sighs too deep for words' – I love that phrase. Sighs can be wordless prayers from body and soul. I sigh a lot of prayers to God. I sigh out to let go of all that pulls me down. I sigh out when I ask for forgiveness or when I'm grateful. Just as a sigh can be a prayer, a gesture with the hand or with the shoulders also can be a wordless prayer. It is any movement that expresses a feeling or thought that can't be put into words. A tear is also a prayer when you give it to God.

WORDLESS PRAYER AND SILENCE

The wordless prayer can also just be silence. Silence is a scarcity in this day and age. There is constant noise and visual inputs all around us. Needless to say, it is hard to hear someone speak to you, if you are in a place filled with noise and your attention is divided between lots of things. God is hard to hear in the midst of our mental 'noise.' Our brains are so busy being engaged in everything surrounding us, and yet we still are disappointed when we don't feel that God is answering our prayers. We pray to God for an answer, but we are too busy or in too much noise to hear it.

God often speaks in the silence where we can pay attention to God's voice. God communicates through scripture, words in a sermon, ideas, pictures or even the encouragement of friends. Sometimes it can be so subtle, that we doubt we heard God right. If you long for an answer from God you might get the idea that God is not answering because 'I am not good enough at being quiet and still.' This is of course not right. We don't earn an answer from God because we are quiet. But when we are quiet the chance of hearing what God is saying is bigger.

If you miss God's presence in your life, plan to spend more time with God. Cut out some of the noise in your life. Turn off Netflix, the News or your phone. Pay attention to God. And here is very important news to all of us active people: you don't have to sit still to quiet your mind! Some of us move in yoga, some spend time in their garden, and some do walking or even running meditations. But all is done with the purpose of quieting down the mind and opening one's heart to God's voice. Some of my big encounters with God often happen on the yoga mat, while running or or when listening to worship music. Silence is tuning in towards God, and being present with God without using words. It is experiencing simplicity and a connection to God. How we do this, depends on who we are.

THE BODY IS MORE THAN AN EMPTY SHELL

In some Christian settings it may seem as if the brain or 'understanding' the theology is the most important aspect in faith. The body is less important – or even something that will lead one only into sin. This perspective, however, is not the concept of the body which we find in the Bible. Everything we are, body as well as mind and intellect, is affected by sin. But at the same time, our body, soul and mind are created in the image of God, and thereby bear a reflection of God. Therefore there is no ranking of body, soul and mind in the Bible.

In the Bible the body is mentioned in many places. Here I mention a few of them. A classic example of the worth of our body is to be found in 1 Corinthians 6:19, 20 (NIV) where Paul says:

> *Or do you not know that your body is a temple of the Holy Spirit within you, which you have from God, and that you are not your own? For you were bought with a price; therefore glorify God in your body.*

Our body is created to be an holy temple of God. The Temple in Jerusalem was in Jewish culture the most holy place on earth dedicated to the worship of God. It was the place where God's presence dwelt, and the place where one went for prayer or sacrifice for the forgiveness of sins. The Temple was a beautiful place that took many years to build. It cost much as materials were gold, silver and expensive wood. Only the best of the best was used in the Temple. Paul compares this Temple with our bodies. This is no small or insignificant comparison he makes. Our bodies are not a shack! But our bodies are also not something we worship, as we see many do today with hyper-focus on how to eat or exercise. The Temple was a place where the worship of God took place.

The body is also mentioned many times in The Book of Psalms. There you'll also find passages which speak of 'body and movement.' In many of the psalms you'll find that the body is used in prayers, or as a way of expressing gratitude when the burden of sin or pain has been removed by God. The psalms are not only about understanding God, but about seeking God with all we are. The body is more than a servant to the brain. In a healthy human life, brain and body co-work in mutual respect for each other's strengths and flaws.

I'll briefly mention a few other perspectives on 'body' in the Bible. In The Lord's Prayer (Matthew 6:9), we pray that we may be provided with daily bread to feed our bodies. The description we find of Heaven in the Bible also speaks of bodies, not just souls. Jesus healed bodies, while at the same time, proclaiming the Kingdom of God. Preaching was not the only focus Jesus had. He was showing the world that physical healing is what is in store for us in Heaven. Health, love and mental peace are what our bodies originally were created for, but sin messed this up. I'm not attempting to write a long and complicated explanation of the theology of the body, only emphasizing that the Bible does not rank the body beneath or above the intellect.

AN HOLISTIC PERSPECTIVE

We often tend to simplify the relation between body, soul, mind and intellect. The correlation is highly complex. We still do not know exactly how these different aspects of a person affect each other. We only know that they do impact each other.

This book is based on the belief that humans are whole beings with all parts working together. Postures or movements can influence our emotions and our thinking, as well as the other way around. This is the reason why people who suffer from depression are encouraged to do some physical activity, together with therapy. It does us good to move our bodies. Of course, all physical movement can be overdone, and end up being not healthy at all. But this should not keep us from physical activity.

The movements and postures we use again and again, affect us. It's not magic but the repetition, I believe, is the big game changer. If we sit all scrunched up when we pray, we may 'protect' our inner organs, but we stop them from working as freely as they could. We partly close the passage of breathing which makes breathing harder. We may appear to be looking down in a sort of 'guilty' position. This scrunch expresses a 'closed' attitude, humble or maybe shameful. If this is our primary position of prayer, I would suggest that it affects our perception of God. For instance, it can be hard to be playful, grateful or happy in such a position. We naturally show our emotions with our body if we are not held back by tradition, culture, group pressure or trauma.

If we pray standing with our palms open outward, shoulders slightly back, we make room in our chest for breathing and for the internal organs to function correctly. We can open up the body even more by leaning the head back and looking up. In this way the body is both vulnerable and in a 'receiving' position. If the arms are lifted upward, or to the sides, we will experience the body as even more open to expressing longing or worship. Different postures can be used intentionally in this way. I believe that no posture can be perceived as 'wrong' in prayer unless it is the one and only posture you use.

Does God hear us better, if we stand in an 'open' position or fold our hands in a certain way? No, but we can help our body and emotions 'experience' God in a new way if we use our bodies purposefully. We can allow our body, prayer, and the subject on which we contemplate to be intertwined, exactly as we normally do when we communicate with one another. We do not greet a dear friend standing with our arms crossed wearing an uncommunicative facial expression...unless perhaps we are joking with our friend! Do not only pray with words. Allow your body language to express your prayers to God. Movements can be just as much worship or surrender, as music and singing are. I believe that people with a healthy image of God will benefit from using the body in different ways for prayer and devotion.

You might be a cautious person and think that new physical positions are strange to perform in the beginning. You'll get used to them if you try. Following, you will see some examples of how to use your body in prayer. Try them out and do not be put off by a new position – just stay in it and try to repeat it for a few days. There is a first for everything. Feel free to create your own variations of the poses.

This concludes our chapter on why poses and movement are recommended in churches, as well as in your own personal devotion time. In this book movement and breath are connected with meditation. You don't have to move or do poses before meditating, but sometimes it helps us calm our mind and enables us better to focus on the meditation.

Opening and receiving

Focus

Receive love

Prayer

Worship, surrender and longing

17

CHRISTIAN MEDITATION - A BRIEF INTRODUCTION

Meditation can be defined as focusing your thoughts and/or mind on one thing only.[1]
Perhaps you have heard that meditation is 'quieting' your mind. This is also true. We quiet our minds by focusing our thoughts on one thing only, as opposed to letting our thoughts wander off, as they often do. Quieting the mind is not 'emptying' the brain as some might suggest, or avoiding thinking of anything at all. Christian meditation as presented in this book is defined as focusing the thoughts, thereby to find a quiet space in which to listen to God, or to rest in the presence of God.

DIFFERENT TYPES OF MEDITATION AND DIFFERENT APPROACHES

Christian meditation has been around since at least the time of King David (1000 BC.) This long tradition has been crossed with different methods, and has resulted in Christian meditation not being limited to just

---

1. *I'll not focus on the difference between contemplation and meditation. The word 'meditation' is used in this book in the form that most people understand it today. The early Church used the word 'contemplation' for what most of us today understand as meditation.*

one way of practice. Meditation can be 'picture meditation' (looking at a painting or image), visualization (using your imagination, for example, seeing yourself walking somewhere), a rosary meditation, or music meditation, just to mention a few.

I would suggest that Christian meditation is not the same as traditional prayer. When we pray, our thoughts naturally wander in different directions – because we pray for different things. Reading a passage in scripture will typically not be meditation either. But by reading only a few verses, focusing on them, and allowing a single word or phrase to be opened up by the Holy Spirit of God, can be defined as a form of meditation. (Some might know the method called 'Lectio Divina' where you are encouraged to ponder and focus on just a few Bible verses.)

The meditations in this book are related to 'The Jesus Meditation.' The Jesus Prayer is a simple form of prayer originating from the Eastern Orthodox Church. This prayer is believed to have developed during the 14th century. The Jesus Prayer was inspired by the prayer or plea of the blind beggar Bartimæus to Jesus: 'Jesus, Son of David, have mercy on me!' (Mark 10:47 NIV) When practicing it, the tradition tells us that you would typically use these words: 'Lord Jesus Christ, Son of God' (when inhaling), 'Have mercy on me, a sinner' (when exhaling.) Or even more simply: 'Lord Jesus (inhale), have mercy on me (exhale).' Some call this kind of meditation 'breath prayer.'

The meditations in this book are also related to another form of meditation called 'centering prayer.' According to Thomas Keating this type of meditation uses a mantra that is repeated. Neither the pace of the breath nor the words you repeat should be your focus or should preoccupy you. Furthermore, you are encouraged to use the same words every time you meditate. The purpose of centering prayer is complete silence. The words or your mantra is only the tool you use to enter into God's peace and silence. When you get to your quiet place you stop repeating the word. When thoughts enter the mind, you repeat the words again until you are in silence.

As mentioned in the Introduction of this book, meditation is a challenge for a lot of us, in particular, if the goal is complete silence. I assume that it is rewarding to find complete silence, but I personally have never experienced it. It takes time and dedication, over a long period of time, to encounter complete silence. It would be nice to experience this, but as for now, I would rather not give up on meditation, but instead practice the way meditations are described in this book. It does not require lots of time, and is still very useful and rewarding in my humble opinion. Maybe one day I will feel called into more deeper and longer meditation, but for now I love meditating on Bible verses without trying to empty my mind.

CHRISTIAN MEDITATION IN THIS BOOK - HOW TO?

The question is, what then is meditation in this book? It is primarily mantra meditation – although not entirely. Mantra meditation is repeating a short scripture verse, aligned with your breathing.

The scripture verses differ from day to day. A complete silence of the mind is not the goal, as it is in centering prayer. The meditations in this book are based on the idea that words from scripture in themselves have great value. Psalm 1 reminds us to contemplate or meditate day and night on the law of God. 'The law of God' meaning the Word of God – verses from scripture.

> *Psalm 1:1-3 NRSV*
> *Happy are those who do not follow*
> *the advice of the wicked,*
> *or take the path that sinners tread,*
> *or sit in the seat of scoffers;*
> *but their delight is in the law of the LORD,*
> *and on his law they meditate day and night.*
> *They are like trees planted by streams of water,*
> *which yield their fruit in its season,*
> *and their leaves do not wither.*
> *In all they do, they prosper.*

Words from scripture are not magical in the sense that they work as 'incantations' with the ability to change soul and mind once uttered. However, it is my conviction that scripture verses also are not like words from any random novel or history book. The Scriptures contain wisdom and depth, when repeated within ourselves, are healthy to meditate on no matter what religious beliefs we hold. Furthermore, if we ask the Holy Spirit to open up the meaning of the words, something unique can happen to us.

My experience with mantra meditation is that scripture verses 'stick with you.' If I have trouble falling asleep, I like to find a calming scripture verse and meditate on it for a while. If I am frustrated about something - one of the Bible verses might pop up in my head and remind me just what is important in this situation and what is not. In this way, I find there are some fantastic benefits in using scripture verses as meditation words or mantras. You will likely find your favorites – just embrace them.

---

2. *Open Mind, Open Heart by Thomas Keating.*

Modern brain science also finds that the repetition of words can change the way neurons are wired in your brain, meaning the way you think about yourself, others, and the world around you. So instead of repeating in your brain: 'I can't' or 'I'm not good enough,' why not repeat: 'I am a child of God' or 'God is faithful and will create a way out.' The more you repeat affirming words, the more likely you will start to believe the words and act on them.

The repetition of words also stills your thoughts and helps you focus. But it opens you up to more than that. When you recite a scripture verse aligned with your breathing, the words might remind you of something in your everyday life. An example like the mantra: 'Your kingdom come ◆ Your will be done' (Matthew 6:10. NIV), might lead your thoughts to how the Kingdom of God could be manifested in your workplace. This might make you want to pray for the love of God in a certain situation at work. These godly thoughts popping up are quite different from thoughts dealing with everyday matters, such as the need to unload your washer. Intuitive thoughts, or what I like to call 'whispers from the Holy Spirit,' you also can freely embrace in your meditations. Then let this 'whisper' form itself into a short prayer. For example: 'God, let your Kingdom be promoted at my workplace.' After this, return to your word of meditation, so the prayer does not steal focus from the meditation you are doing.

In the process of writing this book, I have had numerous intuitive thoughts or 'whispers' about the writing during meditations on scripture. When an idea popped up, I gave it to God, resting assured that if it was important and was meant to go in the book, then the idea would still be there, when I was done meditating. This proved to be the case. Meditation as used in this book, can be illustrated by a circle with a dot in the middle. The dot is the scripture you repeat. The space within the circle is the prayer or reminders from God about the mantra you are reciting. The space outside the circle represents the thoughts that should not fill your mind while meditating (e.g., things on your 'to do' list, worries, noise around you.) While meditating, we try to focus on 'the dot.' Prayers, longings or ideas might pop up, as discussed. Give them all to God and try not to be caught up in them, but return to reciting the verse.

If you prefer to use the scripture verse as a way to total silence as in centering prayer, feel free to do so.

FINAL COMMENTS

When you recite the words in your head, use a soft and calm mental 'voice.' It is crucial that you do not attempt to analyze the words. If you are used to focusing on the understanding of the Bible, it can be difficult to let go of 'text analysis.'

If you are the kind of person who finds it crucial to understand new things 'correctly' from the very beginning, then I urge you to try and let go a little of this side of you. Use the devotionals in this book to focus on just being present with God. Do not focus on 'perfecting' a method or obtaining a certain experience! Be with whatever God has for you today no matter the feeling of success or not.

As mentioned, mantra meditation is just one type of meditation in this book. You will also be asked to imagine or visualize stories. In this way you will be introduced to a number of different forms of meditation. We as individuals are quite different from one another, and so will be our preference for different forms of meditation. One form is not more 'correct' or 'true' than another. My hope for the meditations of this book is that you may find stillness and joy in the meditation – no matter which type of meditation you might prefer.

HOW TO USE THE BOOK

This book is meant to be a source of inspiration for all who desire to involve body and movements in meditation and personal time with God. The book is divided into fifteen themes or chapters. You are free to choose any subject you like in random order, or go through the book from start to finish.
The following compose a common thread in all the devotions of this book:

1. Initiating prayer (this is the same for all devotions of a certain theme.)
2. Calm movements, which are illustrated in the photos in the back of the book. (I know many who use this book without doing any postures, and of course this is possible as well.)
3. Reading of a scripture verse or text.
4. 'Interlude' which is comprised of a text connected to the accompanying scripture verse. (In the Interlude portion I use both short visual meditations and creative approaches, or ways you can use your body in the devotion.)
5. Mantra – meditation word – which is used aligned with your breathing.

In the following pages, I will walk you through the steps mentioned above on how to use this book for the most benefit.

GETTING READY

Before you start, you might want to get out a yoga mat. You might not need one, but if you are going to do exercises with your hands on the floor, it is nice to have one. Try finding a mat no thicker than 6 mm, and one which is not too slippery, as it will make the movements difficult. Find a quiet place and grab your book. You don't need to wear fitness clothes, but you might not want to wear tight pants or clothing.

PRAYING

Every chapter or theme starts with a prayer. Read this or say a short impromptu prayer over the topic of the devotion. Feel free to take some deep breaths. Also don't hold back from sighing when you exhale – it can be very redeeming.

MOVE SLOWLY AND 'PERFORMANCE FREE' FOR ABOUT FIVE MINUTES OR MORE

Find the routines or sequences that you like in the back of the book. You will find three levels. In spite of any physical challenges you might have, you can find something that will work for you! The routines may look more difficult than they actually are, so don't give up before you have tried them a couple of times.

- Easy routines (subtle poses done while sitting on the floor or on a chair.)
- Intermediate routines (mostly standing poses.)
- Challenging routines (poses which require balancing.)

If you are not used to a lot of physical activity, then start out with the Easy routines, and let your body get used to the movements. Try to align your breathing so that you inhale and exhale once per pose, or as you move in and out of a pose.

If you find yourself concentrating too much on aligning your breathing, then just breathe in a way that feels natural to you. Aligned breathing can feel odd to begin with, but it is very rewarding once aligned.
When you have learned the routines by heart, try closing your eyes while doing them. This will help you focus. This is not recommended when it comes to the balance poses, as they become quite difficult when you do not fix your eyes on a focal point. Feel free to sigh aloud when you do the routines.

Should you want to stay in one pose longer than one breath, feel absolutely free to do so. Do you want to avoid a certain pose, just do so. If you want to move your arms, hands or legs in a different way than shown in the picture, feel free. You are your own instructor. You know if it is time to sigh, look up, spread out your arms, etc. The movements become an expression of your spiritual longings, even if you cannot put this in words or even understand it yourself.

The meditation words are not meant to be recited while you move. It can be stressful to move, breathe, and remember words at the same time. When you move, let your thoughts follow the movements and the breathing. You are not doing anything wrong if you do not feel a 'special' presence of God while practicing. Think of your body as a musical instrument. Can an instrument be used to praise God? Can an instrument express feelings and emotions when played? The answer is YES! And the wonderful thing is that music works 'around our intellect.' The body is a kind of God-given 'instrument', which allows us to express ourselves. Let your body talk to God through the movements without the need to intellectualize.

I recommend that you spend time learning one or two routines by heart. When you are familiar with the movements, you can mix the routines as you like. Feel free to make up your own favorite routine out of the ones in the book.

The photos of each routine are taken in a way that makes it easy for you to understand how to do the pose. You are not meant to turn on the yoga mat, even if it may look like that in the photo. The pose has been shown from different angles in order to explain it better.
Repeat the routines as many times as you like. A good suggestion is for at least five minutes. Some days you may feel like more movement to help your wandering thoughts calm down. Other days you may need complete quietness around you. While still on others you might enjoy music accompaniment.

The movement part is set at the beginning of the devotion for two reasons. The one being that movement and deep breathing can help quiet the mind and thoughts. This prepares us for the meditation. The other reason being that the intention of the movement is to be 'open' to God. This means freeing your body to play its own 'music' to God, by avoiding your analytic mind. Remember, you worship God with your body and the body is the temple of God (1 Corinthians 6:19.)

When you move, remember that you are on 'the playground of God.' Let go of all the thoughts about 'perfecting' a pose or improving it from the last time. Remember, the movements and poses should be 'performance free.' As I mentioned before – you might not pray or even feel something special while moving.

READ THE SCRIPTURE VERSE

Read the text you have chosen slowly, either to yourself or out loud. Be open to whatever God might want to remind you of, while reading. Perhaps there is a specific word that pops out and makes sense to you in a special way.

THE INTERLUDE

Read this and let the actions, movements or visualizations speak to your imagination or your senses. Interlude is not a deep theological reflection. Interlude is an opportunity to allow the text you read and its essence to become 'present' with you as you use your senses.

MEDITATE USING THE SCRIPTURE VERSE

When you meditate, sit with a straight back on the floor or a firm chair. Alternatively, you may lie down. If you fall asleep easily, then sit up. It is important that your body position does not disturb your meditation. If you sit cross-legged and are not used to it, you will probably get a tired back and hips after just a few minutes. If you would like to practice sitting on the floor, then start your meditation there, and move to a chair when you feel your concentration disappearing because of discomfort in the position. Recite to yourself the meditation words aligned with your breathing.

And please remember that there is nothing so disturbing in a meditation as keeping an eye on the time. So set an alarm for five or ten minutes, and try concentrating for this period of time. It is crucial that the alarm sound level is very low, so you are not startled when the alarm goes off. You might want to opt for a phone vibration alarm instead. Being startled suddenly when you have been calm for some time can undo some of the good you have just accomplished.

YOU MIGHT ALSO LIKE TO KNOW

The scriptures used in the meditations – 'mantras' are often a bit shorter than you will find in some Bible versions. This is to make it easier to align the breathing and the words. The goal has been to keep the words as close to the original as possible.

THE ACT OF BREATHING DEEPLY

Begin by noticing your natural breath. Notice how your belly and rib cage expand on your inhale, and how they contract on your exhale. Make sure your shoulders are relaxed. We mainly work with our diaphragm when we take a deep breath. If you breathe superficially and/or lift your shoulders as you inhale, you are not using the full capacity of your lungs. If you are stressed or anxious, your breathing is often rapid and shallow. As mentioned earlier, this does no good to calm your nervous system when you are about to meditate. Try to get your breath to go as deeply as possible and use a few more seconds on each breath. It might take some time to calm your breathing, but this is normal. Give yourself time. Accept and respect your own body's time and pace necessary to relax and slow down.

When we meditate it is important that we breathe calmly but not too slowly. If you get dizzy or feel uncomfortable, the reason might be that you are not getting enough air because your breath is too slow. Find the pace of a natural yet deep breath and then begin your meditation.

MOVEMENT IS HEALTHY IF YOU LISTEN TO YOUR BODY

This book claims that movement is healthy and good for your body, but of course there are exceptions. If you have knee or back injuries, there are certain movements you need to approach with caution. Whenever you move, listen to your body. If you feel a sharp pain, it is a sign from the body to you that you should back off and maybe not go as deep or low in the position as you have.

Remember that your muscles become stiff and weaken if you sit in a chair for a long period of time every day. This is the reason why it is healthy for you to move, and of course with caution, if you are not used to any kind of exercise or movement. Your body needs to stretch and you need to strengthen muscles for your musculoskeletal system to work optimally. Stiff or tight muscles and tendons often equal pain in the body. The body is connected from top to toe and the different parts of the body affect each other. An example would be: if you are stiff or sore in your right hip, you start to walk differently to compensate for the pain by using your left hip and thigh muscles more. This means that you might start to feel pain in the entire back, and even in your shoulders, as muscles along the spine are all connected to the top of your spine. Then you might have headaches because of stiffness in your shoulders. And so on - you get the picture.

By using the postures and movements as shown in this book, you will help yourself to less pain in the long run. Using the movements regularly, helps you get your body back on track with less pain. Your musculoskeletal system becomes more balanced, and this is healthier for you.

POSTURES AND MOVEMENTS TO BE EXTRA MINDFUL OF

BACK BENDS

The spine is primarily designed to bend forward, so this means that the spine is challenged when we do back bends, either standing or sitting down. Typically it is the lower part of the back that is the weak part. If you have had lower back issues or pain in the past, be very mindful when leaning back. Make sure you engage your abdominal muscles as you lean backward. You might even put your hands on your lower back for extra support. Avoid seeing how low you can go, especially if you are not warmed up.
Most people can benefit from doing back bends, but be mindful of your own limitations.

THE NECK IN BACK BENDS

When you do back bends, you can let your head fall back and thereby stretch out your throat. If you have neck problems this might feel uncomfortable. In that case, tuck in your chin towards the chest as you lean back. You might even fold your hands behind the head to hold onto your head. Back bends are still great, even if the neck and throat are not included in the stretch.

HYPEREXTENDED KNEES AND ELBOWS

Many have a tendency to hyperextend their elbows or knees. It can be a hard habit to get rid of and it might require your full attention every time you use these joints. Often, the reason it can feel nice to hyperextend joints is then the surrounding muscles need to work less. For example, if the pressure of standing is directed toward the knee joint instead of the muscles in the thigh, those muscles are less engaged. Hyperextension is unhealthy for you because of the bones and ligaments positioned around the outer edge of the joint. This, combined with the fact that joints often carry a lot of our bodyweight, means that hyperextension can lead to osteoarthritis over time. To avoid this, try always to microbend the knee and elbow, in balance or plank poses. Be mindful, as it takes some effort to get rid of the habit.

INVERSIONS - WHEN HEAD IS LOWER THAN HEART

Some people get dizzy or otherwise uncomfortable if they have their head down for longer than a few moments. This might be due to low blood pressure. There are some options if you don't want to have your head down for too long. Instead of going into a forward fold (inversion), try to keep your head and heart aligned on an invisible horizontal line. Make sure to engage your core muscles and/or keep your hands on your thighs. In this pose you will not get the full benefit of the forward fold (stretch in your lower back and hamstrings) but you will still be moving and using your body.

THE
DEVOTIONS

THE LOVE OF GOD AND MEANING OF LOVE

'The meaning of life is love' you might have heard people say.
But the actual essence of love can be hard to grasp. What is love for instance, if we are not talking about being IN love. How does it feel? It becomes even more difficult when we speak of love for God and the love from God. God is invisible, omnipresent and all-powerful. But God is also our sovereign, parent, savior, protector and friend.

How can we experience love from God?
There is no simple answer to that.
In this chapter, you will be asked to focus on a physical experience of the love of God, rather than try to perceive it intellectually. There is a big difference between understanding or hearing about the love of God, and then having the certainty of it carved in your body and soul.
If you have a hard time receiving love, gifts or kind words from others, you might find it hard to receive God's love. Your brain might not be 'wired' to accept love given freely and unconditionally, due to a number of factors. When you repeat the words in the meditations regarding love during these devotions, try to let the words sink into your heart and let the words and God's Spirit 'rewire' your brain. The meditations will give you an experience of God's love in a new way, and help build the certainty of God's love into you. You do not have to 'pull yourself together,' behave in an 'holy' way or even pray a lot. You are loved by God before you do anything to earn it. Just practice receiving the love of God by 'being present' in it, rather than intellectually trying to understand it.

PRAYER

God, Your love encompasses
everything,
it is the living beat of the world.
Help me to open myself to it
like eranthis and anemones
stretching towards the sun.
Let Your love flow through me
toward the rest of creation.
Let me see the world as movable.
Let me see the person I meet with
Your eyes.

LOVE ◆
NEVER ENDS

MAKE SLOW MOVEMENTS
WITH DEEP BREATHS

Read 1 Corinthians 13:1-13 NIV

If I speak in the tongues of men or of angels, but do not have love, I am only a resounding gong or a clanging cymbal.

If I have the gift of prophecy and can fathom all mysteries and all knowledge, and if I have a faith that can move mountains, but do not have love, I am nothing.

If I give all I possess to the poor and give over my body to hardship that I may boast, but do not have love, I gain nothing.

Love is patient, love is kind. It does not envy, it does not boast, it is not proud. It does not dishonor others, it is not self-seeking, it is not easily angered, it keeps no record of wrongs.

Love does not delight in evil but rejoices with the truth.

It always protects, always trusts, always hopes, always perseveres.

Love never fails. But where there are prophecies, they will cease; where there are tongues, they will be stilled; where there is knowledge, it will pass away.

For we know in part and we prophesy in part,

but when completeness comes, what is in part disappears.

When I was a child, I talked like a child, I thought like a child, I reasoned like a child. When I became a man, I put the ways of childhood behind me.

For now we see only a reflection as in a mirror; then we shall see face to face. Now I know in part; then I shall know fully, even as I am fully known.

And now these three remain: faith, hope and love. But the greatest of these is love.

Read the following text again and replace the word 'love' with 'God.' Read slowly, almost like you are 'chewing' and 'digesting' each sentence.

God is patient, God is kind. God does not envy, God does not boast, God is not proud. God does not dishonor others, God is not self-seeking, God is not easily angered, God keeps no record of wrongs. God does not delight in evil but rejoices with the truth. God always protects, always trusts, always hopes, always perseveres. God never fails.

Sit for a moment and let the descriptions of God sink in. Is there a specific part that touches your heart? Maybe these are some words that you need to hear today.

MEDITATION

I INHALE AND BEGIN WITH...

LOVE ◆ NEVER CEASES

GOD DELIGHTS IN ME ◆

MAKE SLOW MOVEMENTS WITH DEEP BREATHS

Read Zephaniah 3: 17-18 NRSV

The LORD, your God, is in your midst, a warrior who gives victory; he will rejoice over you with gladness, he will renew you in his love; he will exult over you with loud singing as on a day of festival. I will remove disaster from you, so that you will not bear reproach for it.

INTERLUDE

Close your eyes for a moment after reading this text.
Use your imagination and picture yourself standing in front of a closed door. The door opens and you see Jesus standing there. Picture the smile on his face when he sees you. He gives you a huge hug and welcomes you into the house. To your surprise there is a party going on. A party that Jesus made for you and you alone. You have the choice to stay outside the door and just look in. Or you can take a few steps inside the house and allow yourself to receive what has been prepared for you. Observe the happy people there and see Jesus clapping his hands to the beat of the music. Maybe he invites you to dance with him. Feel the joy and delight he has in you.

Stay in this visual meditation for a moment.
Jesus did not only throw you a party. He did so much more for you, as he walked the long road to his crucifixion. He walked the road and suffered for you not because he had to. He did it because he delights in you and desires to spend eternity with you. This is how much Jesus loves you!

MEDITATION

I INHALE AND BEGIN WITH...

GOD DELIGHTS ◆ IN ME
Eventually prolong the meditation with the following sentence:
SHOWS HIS LOVE ◆ AGAIN

NOTHING CAN SEPARATE ME FROM GOD'S LOVE

MAKE SLOW MOVEMENTS WITH DEEP BREATHS

Read Romans 8: 31-39 NIV

What, then, shall we say in response to these things? If God is for us, who can be against us? He who did not spare his own Son, but gave him up for us all—how will he not also, along with him, graciously give us all things? Who will bring any charge against those whom God has chosen? It is God who justifies. Who then is the one who condemns? No one. Christ Jesus who died—more than that, who was raised to life—is at the right hand of God and is also interceding for us. Who shall separate us from the love of Christ? Shall trouble or hardship or persecution or famine or nakedness or danger or sword?

As it is written: 'For your sake we face death all day long; we are considered as sheep to be slaughtered.'

No, in all these things we are more than conquerors through him who loved us. For I am convinced that neither death nor life, neither angels nor demons, neither the present nor the future, nor any powers, neither height nor depth, nor anything else in all creation, will be able to separate us from the love of God that is in Christ Jesus our Lord.

If you know that you somehow are used to 'pleasing others' in order to receive love or feel worthy, try to notice how the following statement feels. You are never going to make God love you more! No matter how hard you try to serve God or try to make God happy, it changes nothing. Why?

Because you are loved fully and completely already. It has nothing to do with what you can or cannot do, how you serve others, or how nice you behave. You are loved no matter what.

More actions or less will not make God love you more or less. God will always love you 100%!

MEDITATION

INHALE AND BEGIN WITH...

NOTHING CAN SEPARATE ME ◆ FROM GOD'S LOVE

PEACE

If you follow the News the word 'peace' is not the
first thing that comes to our minds. Peace does
not seem to describe the world today. When I talk with
colleagues, friends or neighbors peace seems to be something everyone
is longing for. It can be peace from a stressful situation, peace from the
fast pace in life, or peace in a relationship.
Where can one find peace today? Some find peace in
yoga. Here one is offered peace through movement,
breath and meditation. But even the peace found in yoga
practice does not last forever. It can disappear when you
leave the studio and go back to work or home.
What people might offer and what may feel good for a passing
moment, does not solve the main problem in our souls. In the
New Testament we are told that everlasting peace is found in
believing in Jesus Christ. I believe that only Jesus can meet us
in our deep spiritual longing for peace, meaning in life and love.
Through Jesus and in God we can have permanent, eternal peace.
This means that we do not have to prove our own worth in this
world with a new car, beautiful home, perfect family or successful
career. We can receive peace when we dare to lay our lives, pride
and personal ambitions in God's capable hands. God does not
promise us a life with no trouble or sorrow, but God promises
to give us peace, support and help even in troubling times.
Peace in Christ is not something magical which
'happens' to us when we believe. Peace in God
is more like knowing in your heart that even
though it's raining outside, the sky is still
blue above the clouds and the sun will
shine again.

PRAYER

Jesus, pour out Your peace over my body
and my thoughts.
Help me not to be defined by circumstances
but by full knowledge of being your beloved child.
Protect me from whatever will steal my peace.
Let me have a safe space in my heart that I can share
with You.
May I meet this day from that place in me - in You.
From the soles of my feet to the top of my head
may Your peace allow me to speak truth and love
without being harsh or controlled by fear.
Create a deep awareness in me that
everything is in Your hands.

GOD'S PEACE NEVER FAILS

MAKE SLOW MOVEMENTS WITH DEEP BREATHS

Read Isaiah 54: 4-10 NRSV

Do not fear, for you will not be ashamed; do not be discouraged, for you will not suffer disgrace; for you will forget the shame of your youth, and the disgrace of your widowhood you will remember no more. For your Maker is your husband, the LORD of hosts is his name; the Holy One of Israel is your Redeemer, the God of the whole earth he is called. For the LORD has called you like a wife forsaken and grieved in spirit, like the wife of a man's youth when she is cast off, says your God.

For a brief moment I abandoned you, but with great compassion I will gather you. In overflowing wrath for a moment I hid my face from you, but with everlasting love I will have compassion on you, says the LORD, your Redeemer. This is like the days of Noah to me: Just as I swore that the waters of Noah would never again go over the earth, so I have sworn that I will not be angry with you and will not rebuke you. For the mountains may depart and the hills be removed, but my steadfast love shall not depart from you, and my covenant of peace shall not be removed, says the LORD, who has compassion on you.

INTERLUDE

Find a candle. Light it and gaze into it from a safe distance. If you do not have a candle nearby, picture one in your mind.

Notice how the light spreads out. Meditate on God's peace, as the light dissolves the darkness. Picture how you can carry this candle or light into the 'dark' situations in your own life - situations where peace is missing. Let the flickering, calm light of this candle dissolve that darkness. Ask for God's peace to grow in these places in your life.

MEDITATION

INHALE AND BEGIN WITH...

GOD'S PEACE ◆ NEVER FAILS

You can prolong the meditation with the following sentence:

GOD'S LOVE ◆ IS STEADFAST

MAY THE HOPE OF GOD ◆ FILL ME WITH PEACE

MAKE SLOW MOVEMENTS WITH DEEP BREATHS

Read Romans 15: 13 NRSV

May the God of hope fill you with all joy and peace in believing, so that you may abound in hope by the power of the Holy Spirit.

Close your eyes and try to feel what happens in your chest. You might put your hand on your chest and one on your belly. Notice the rhythm of your breath. You might even feel your heart beating.

Picture that you open up your heart to be filled with God's peace and hope. As you inhale, imagine how you are filled with the Holy Spirit. Inside your chest, picture a bowl, and with every breath let the bowl fill up bit by bit. As your bowl fills up, receive God's peace and contentment.

MEDITATION

INHALE AND BEGIN WITH...

MAY THE HOPE OF GOD ◆ FILL ME WITH PEACE

JESUS IS THE SAME TODAY, TOMORROW AND ALWAYS

MAKE SLOW MOVEMENTS WITH DEEP BREATHS

Read Hebrews 13: 5-8 NRSV

Keep your lives free from the love of money, and be content with what you have; for he has said, 'I will never leave you or forsake you.'
So we can say with confidence, 'The Lord is my helper; I will not be afraid. What can anyone do to me?'
Remember your leaders, those who spoke the word of God to you; consider the outcome of their way of life, and imitate their faith.
Jesus Christ is the same yesterday and today and forever.

If you long for peace, the reason for this might be that you are in the middle of changing circumstances. Maybe you have questions which require answers. Not knowing what to do can make your soul uneasy. Uncertainty is hard for most people. We love being in control.

Today, stand up and find a solid wall and lean up against it. As you lean back still standing on your feet, feel how the wall is supporting your weight. As you lean on the wall, imagine yourself leaning into God's peace. God can carry all you are. Your emotions might come and go, but God's presence is always there. God is the same today, tomorrow and always. God knows your past and knows your present circumstances. Just as the wall supports you, remind yourself that God's faithfulness also supports you. God will never, never, ever abandon you!

MEDITATION

INHALE AND BEGIN WITH...

JESUS IS THE SAME TODAY ◆ TOMORROW AND ALWAYS

SURRENDER

There is freedom and joy, as well as loss and frustration connected with surrendering your life to God. Loss because you no longer can do just what you feel like doing. Or loss because you might have to quit doing some 'activities' you think are merely harmless 'fun.' You might have to change some habits because they do not align with God's plan for your life. But there is also joy and freedom in surrender because God's ways are good, new, exciting and meaningful.

When we listen to God and accept that our lives are not about ourselves, I believe that we find home. We align our lives with the life that God intended from the beginning of creation.

But God's order and prescribed life as outlined in scripture gives new life, purpose and meaning, even if it is a life that does not look like that of your neighbors and co-workers.

You will find ease, freedom and boldness when life and happiness are not dependent on your own competencies, career and ability to choose what is right. There is peace in surrendering control, your inner perfectionist, workaholism, temper, marriage, etc. to God - as well as all the broken and 'imperfect' parts that have the potential to destroy our lives. These might be returned to you in time by God in a renewed form ... cleansed, repaired, made beautiful and holy.

PRAYER

To You from whom all good things come I surrender like a baby bird letting itself fall from its nest to be carried on the wind.
Carry me wherever you wish.
Let me be a round stone, moved by the waves of the sea, safe in life and death, because it all happens in You.

ALL THINGS ◆ ARE CREATED IN GOD

MAKE SLOW MOVEMENTS WITH DEEP BREATHS

Read Colossians 1: 11-19 NRSV

May you be made strong with all the strength that comes from his glorious power, and may you be prepared to endure everything with patience, while joyfully giving thanks to the Father, who has enabled you to share in the inheritance of the saints in the light.

He has rescued us from the power of darkness and transferred us into the kingdom of his beloved Son, in whom we have redemption, the forgiveness of sins. He is the image of the invisible God, the firstborn of all creation; for in him all things in heaven and on earth were created, things visible and invisible, whether thrones or dominions or rulers or powers - all things have been created through him and for him.

He himself is before all things, and in him all things hold together.

He is the head of the body, the church; he is the beginning, the firstborn from the dead, so that he might come to have first place in everything. For in him all the fullness of God was pleased to dwell.

INTERLUDE

God created the earth, the stars and the universe, so infinite and marvelous, that not even the most clever people on earth can fully comprehend it all. God is a mystery who often chooses to work through logic and order. Science we can understand through logic. But sometimes God breaks the normal rules of science and leaves us in wonder. God is creative. Try to picture some of the many odd and awesome animals there are. God made them. God is the maker of the beauty you see in every sunset and sunrise. God is the author of love as we experience it looking into a baby's face or when we are in nurturing relationships. God keeps life going - every heartbeat and every breath. Close your eyes for a moment and let your heart be filled with God's greatness as you meditate on what you have just read.

In our busy everyday life we tend to forget who God is. We get preoccupied with 'navel gazing' and think that we know what is best. We forget how great, almighty and powerful God really is. God knows the past, the present, and the future.

Today I will suggest that you bow down on your knees and get into 'child's pose' (see picture at the front page of the book.) As you are kneeling, thank God for how good God is, and surrender your 'all' to God. Perhaps you might feel like saying something like this:

'God, I am sorry. I believe you know what is best for me, but I tend to forget this. I go 'rogue' at times and think my way is better than yours. Help me get back on track. Help me live with you as God, not me. Please take the driver's seat and just let me sit next to you.'

MEDITATION

I INHALE AND BEGIN WITH...

ALL THINGS ◆ ARE CREATED IN GOD

NOT MY WILL ◆ BUT YOUR WILL

MAKE SLOW MOVEMENTS WITH DEEP BREATHS

Read Luke 22: 39-44 NIV

Jesus went out as usual to the Mount of Olives, and his disciples followed him. On reaching the place, he said to them, 'Pray that you will not fall into temptation.'

He withdrew about a stone's throw beyond them, knelt down and prayed, 'Father, if you are willing, take this cup from me; yet not my will, but yours be done.' An angel from heaven appeared to him and strengthened him. And being in anguish, he prayed more earnestly, and his sweat was like drops of blood falling to the ground.

The text you read describes Jesus' battle with himself, before he is taken captive, whipped and crucified. He knows not only how painful crucifixion will be, but also that he will be abandoned by God, his father.

Find a piece of paper and a pen. Draw a cross on the paper. There is no right or wrong way. Draw a cross and whatever details you wish on the cross. As you are drawing, thank Jesus for what he did for you. He was willing to surrender everything to God because he knew that it meant saving you and me. He kept his eyes focused on Heaven, looking forward to meeting you there.

If it makes sense, draw on the paper below the cross, and write down all that you want to surrender to Christ.

MEDITATION

INHALE AND BEGIN WITH...

NOT MY WILL ◆ BUT YOUR WILL

RESTORE TO ME ◆ THE JOY OF SALVATION

MAKE SLOW MOVEMENTS WITH DEEP BREATHS

Read Psalm 51: 7-12 NIV

Cleanse me with hyssop, and I will be clean;
wash me, and I will be whiter than snow.

Let me hear joy and gladness;
let the bones you have crushed rejoice.

Hide your face from my sins
and blot out all my iniquity.

Create in me a pure heart, O God,
and renew a steadfast spirit within me.

Do not cast me from your presence
or take your Holy Spirit from me.

Restore to me the joy of your salvation
and grant me a willing spirit, to sustain me.

The verses we read talk about sin. It is a hard word for us to understand today. We tend to think of sin as murder or adultery. Or maybe sin is something we don't want to talk about because it might make people run at a fast pace out of the church. It can be helpful to think of sin in other terms - as synonymous with the words – brokenness, disharmony, missing the mark, or torn apart. You can also contemplate about sin as the following:

- Sin is also that which harms our relationship with others. We want to love, but often we feel envy, anger, disappointment, or a need for constant approval. It is what makes us feel like we need to be right all the time, or seek revenge for wrongs.
- Sin is what we do to this earth. We destroy Nature around us with pollution, garbage, and greed.

You might want to read today's verses again in the light of the previous points. You might concentrate on one of the thoughts mentioned. You might get down on your knees, or take 'child's pose.'

After reading the text again and praying it with your heart, remember that you are forgiven! Nothing you have done can change the fact that Jesus died on the Cross for your sins. You are made whiter than snow, cleansed and made pure. The sin that might still try to creep into your life to attempt to hurt you or others, I pray, will be met by God's Spirit and overcoming help and power. A sign of your forgiveness can be the simple washing of your hands. You might go to the sink, pour soap in your hands and wash them. Watch how the soap and the dirt from your hands swirl into the drain. Remind yourself that your soul has been washed clean from all sin.

MEDITATION

I INHALE AND BEGIN WITH...

RESTORE TO ME ◆
THE JOY OF SALVATION

LONGING AND SEARCHING FOR GOD

When you are longing for something it can feel like things are not as they ought to be. As if there are some puzzle pieces missing. Your longing might be a motivation for you to start searching for something. It might be something very concrete, such as searching for a partner in life, the right job, or healing. But it also might be something less concrete, such as searching for meaning in life, or getting to know what God is all about, or even seeking for answers for questions you don't even know how to ask. Your longing can stem from deep in your soul and be expressed as a vague feeling of something important missing.

Our life on this earth will always be somewhat unfulfilled. We were created to live with God in a loving environment. But we are not in Heaven yet. Be mindful not to fulfill your inner longing with material things you can buy or eat. Instead use that longing to seek God. Go out into Nature, pray or read the Bible. Join a community of believers and find out how they live their lives and fulfill their longings. As you open your heart you might be surprised by the things God will show you. There might be other perspectives or answers than you first thought. Please, just trust God and let God's Spirit shape you as God fulfills your heart's longing.

PRAYER

God, with my body, soul and spirit I am longing just as all of Your creation does. You know the depths from which my searching springs.

Please nourish the 'good' longing and let me find You in everything.

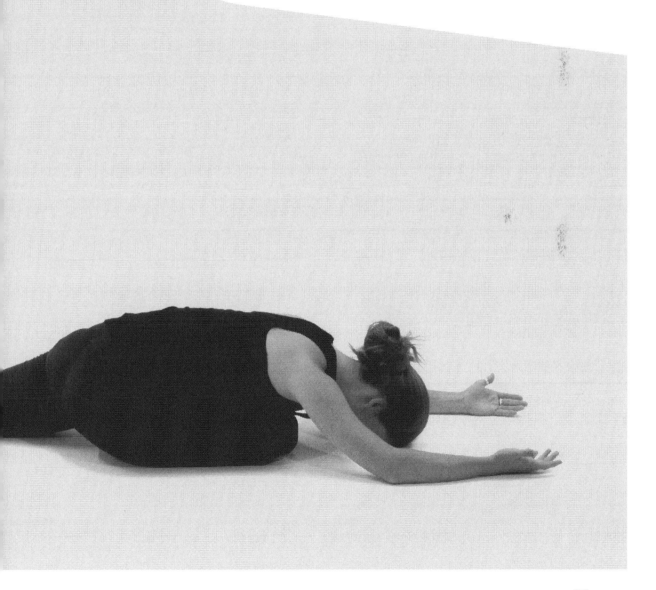

SEEK FIRST ◆
THE KINGDOM OF GOD

MAKE SLOW MOVEMENTS
WITH DEEP BREATHS

Read Matthew 6: 33-34 NIV

But seek first his kingdom and his righteousness, and all these things will be given to you as well. Therefore do not worry about tomorrow, for tomorrow will worry about itself. Each day has enough trouble of its own.

The difficulty about longing and seeking for that elusive 'something' is, we will never really know when or if God will give us exactly what we think we need. The verse reminds us to let go. Let go of the idea that you know what God needs to give you or do for you before you can be truly happy. Let go of the entitlement and the thought 'I deserve this because everybody else has it.' Or: 'I have worked so hard for it, it's not fair if I don't get this.'

Ask yourself if there is anything you need to let go because you think you earned it... or deserve it?

Instead of focusing on what you want, focus on God - His kingdom and righteousness. All the other things you seek might look very different in this perspective. I often have to remind myself that what I often so desperately want might be only a shadow of what God knows is in my best interest.

MEDITATION

I INHALE AND BEGIN WITH...

SEEK FIRST ◆
THE KINGDOM OF GOD

POUR OUT YOUR HEART ◆ TO HIM

MAKE SLOW MOVEMENTS WITH DEEP BREATHS

Read Psalm 62: 5-8 NIV

Yes, my soul, find rest in God;
my hope comes from him.

Truly he is my rock and my salvation;
he is my fortress, I will not be shaken.

My salvation and my honor depend on God;
he is my mighty rock, my refuge.

Trust in him at all times, you people;
pour out your hearts to him,
for God is our refuge.

INTERLUDE

There are no thoughts or feelings that God does not know about. This is the reason why you can pour out your heart to him without holding back. God is that 'safe space.' Are there any deep longings in your heart that you have never prayed about? Something that might be so 'far out' that you never really thought it would make sense to pour this out to God?

As you sit down today, shape your hands into an open bowl in your lap. Picture how your hands are holding a bowl God has given you.

Pour out all your longings into this bowl with no excuses or long explanations. Speak freely like a child talking to Daddy or Mommy. When you feel like you have emptied out your soul, lift up the bowl in your hands above your head. Picture how God takes the bowl from you as a gift. Let God carry your heart's needs and longings.

Let your hands sink into your lap again. This time they are empty and free. Sigh out a few times as a sign of relief and thanks to God.

MEDITATION

I INHALE AND BEGIN WITH...

POUR OUT YOUR HEART ◆ TO HIM

THE ONE WHO CALLS YOU ◆ IS FAITHFUL

MAKE SLOW MOVEMENTS WITH DEEP BREATHS

Read Thessalonians 5: 23-24 NIV

May God himself, the God of peace, sanctify you through and through. May your whole spirit, soul and body be kept blameless at the coming of our Lord Jesus Christ. The one who calls you is faithful, and he will do it.

The Bible speaks of God with many different adjectives. In the verse today God is called 'God of peace.'

Close your eyes and breathe deeply a few times. Try to think back in time and remember a place where you felt peace. Deep peace. Let the memory fill your mind for some moments. Try to picture what the place looked like or what was so peaceful about this memory. You might remember sounds or a distinct scent attached to this memory.

Remind yourself that God is the maker of peace. He created every human heart to contain peace and He can fill your heart with peace now, as well. God is faithful and will meet you in your empty place. There is no injustice, no feeling, no emptiness God's peace cannot reach. Receive this today. Let God fill you.

Stay in the memory as long as you like and thank God for giving you peace back then as well as right now.

MEDITATION

INHALE AND BEGIN WITH...

THE ONE WHO CALLS YOU ◆ IS FAITHFUL

INTO YOUR HANDS ◆ I COMMIT MY SPIRIT

MAKE SLOW MOVEMENTS WITH DEEP BREATHS

Read Psalm 31: 5 NIV

Into your hands I commit my spirit; deliver me, Lord, my faithful God.

Take a close look at your hands. Turn them around, look at the lines in your palm and your unique fingerprints.

Have you ever considered that God has hands?

We are created in God's image so it's not difficult to think that God also has hands. Jesus had hands too. He used them to eat with, heal, and probably 'talk' with as he connected with the crowds. Jesus' hands were also nailed to the Cross.

Close your eyes and picture Jesus on the Cross. Picture his hands pierced with nails and carrying a part of his weight as he hung on the Cross. Jesus' hands not only carried his weight, they also carried all human grief, all sickness, suffering, and death.

During his suffering Jesus spoke about hands. He called out to his father: 'Into Your hands I commend my spirit.' Jesus entrusted his hands and life unto God.

But this is not the end of the story. Jesus rose again and with his pierced hands he blessed his disciples and told them to have faith in him. As you use the meditation words today let your hands make a gesture of their own. Let your hands express a cry for help or show what you might not be able to put into words. Let your hands express your longings.

MEDITATION

I INHALE AND BEGIN WITH...

INTO YOUR HANDS ◆ I COMMIT MY SPIRIT

TRUST

Trust is not something we automatically have for other people. Trust is something that we give, when we experience that people are trustworthy, uphold their promises, are righteous, etc. Trust in God can be a challenge, especially if we have no previous experience with God. This is either because the faith is new or because we do not have a basic trust in the world around us. It can be helpful to ask God for more trust. God knows our hearts anyway.

Listening to other people's experiences with God can be extremely rewarding and help you gain trust in God. To hear how they have experienced trust in God, can help you grow in your faith in God's love for you. Without a fundamental belief in God's love, it is difficult to trust God and His plan for your life.

The Bible repeatedly mentions that God has a tremendous love for humans. It is not a vague love where God says, 'You are good enough' or 'Not that bad.' Or conditional, 'The better you behave, the more I love you.'
No, God's love is specific, concrete and actually independent of our more or less successful attempts to be 'good people.' In the Bible, Jesus tells us that all our head hairs are counted and that there is nothing we can hide from God. God shapes us in our mother's womb and knows all our days before they arrive. God is as interested in you as a good mother or father is interested in their child. With this love as the foundation of your faith, maybe it is easier to have trust in God?

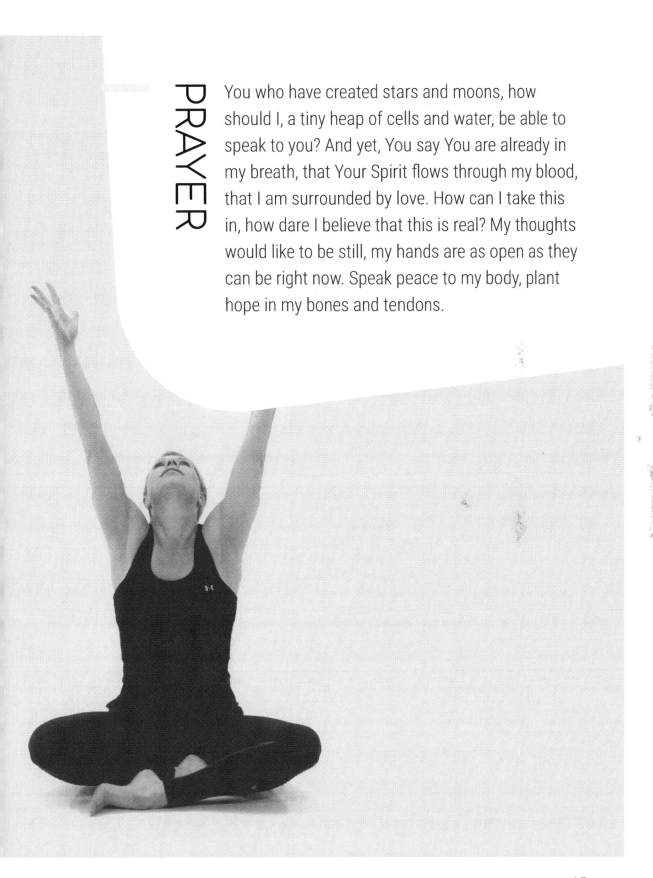

PRAYER

You who have created stars and moons, how should I, a tiny heap of cells and water, be able to speak to you? And yet, You say You are already in my breath, that Your Spirit flows through my blood, that I am surrounded by love. How can I take this in, how dare I believe that this is real? My thoughts would like to be still, my hands are as open as they can be right now. Speak peace to my body, plant hope in my bones and tendons.

NOTHING IS IMPOSSIBLE ◆ WITH GOD

MAKE SLOW MOVEMENTS WITH DEEP BREATHS

Read Luke 1: 26-38 The Message

In the sixth month of Elizabeth's pregnancy, God sent the angel Gabriel to the Galilean village of Nazareth to a virgin engaged to be married to a man descended from David. His name was Joseph, and the virgin's name, Mary. Upon entering, Gabriel greeted her:

Good morning! You're beautiful with God's beauty. Beautiful inside and out! God be with you.

She was thoroughly shaken, wondering what was behind a greeting like that. But the angel assured her, 'Mary, you have nothing to fear. God has a surprise for you: You will become pregnant and give birth to a son and call his name Jesus.

He will be great, be called 'Son of the Highest.'

The Lord God will give him the throne of his father David; He will rule Jacob's house forever— no end, ever, to his kingdom.'

Mary said to the angel, 'But how? I've never slept with a man.'

The angel answered, 'The Holy Spirit will come upon you, the power of the Highest hover over you;

Therefore, the child you bring to birth will be called Holy, Son of God. And did you know that your cousin Elizabeth conceived a son, old as she is? Everyone called her barren, and here she is six months pregnant! Nothing, you see, is impossible with God.'

And Mary said, 'Yes, I see it all now: I'm the Lord's maid, ready to serve. Let it be with me just as you say.' Then the angel left her.

INTERLUDE

It's a crazy situation Mary is in. She is young and inexperienced in many ways. Notice how the angel comforts her and speaks into her fear and doubt. Mary is not afraid to speak her mind and be honest as she communicates with the angel. It says something very important about her trust in God's love.

The text might remind you of a situation where you have to choose between some things. Maybe you want to try something new or feel like God is calling you - but think it is too hard. You feel you might not have the courage to follow your dream or let go of what you know. Stepping into new things can be really hard because we know what we have but not what we will get.
No matter your situation, the first step could be to ponder today's verse: 'Nothing is impossible with God.' You might not know the steps ahead or you might be afraid to take the next step. Just know: 'Nothing is impossible with God.'
Before meditating speak the words aloud: 'Nothing is impossible with God.'
Say the sentence a few times and as you speak it, emphasize different words in the sentence. NOTHING is impossible with God. Nothing IS impossible with God. Nothing is impossible with GOD.

MEDITATION

INHALE AND BEGIN WITH...

NOTHING IS IMPOSSIBLE ◆ WITH GOD

MY HEART IS SAFE ◆
I TRUST THE LORD

MAKE SLOW MOVEMENTS
WITH DEEP BREATHS

Read Psalm 112: 5-7 NRSV

It is well with those who deal generously and lend, who conduct their affairs with justice. For the righteous will never be moved; they will be remembered forever. They are not afraid of evil tidings; their hearts are firm, secure in the LORD.

INTERLUDE

Stand up, spread your arms out to the sides beside your hips with your palms facing forward (mountain pose.) Breathe deeply and slowly a few times. You can make a slight back bend with a few breaths.

You are standing open and vulnerable because your arms are not protecting your vital organs (heart, lungs, kidneys etc.)

For some, the position is anxiety-producing. The purpose is not to provoke anxiety, but to open oneself to be vulnerable. It is precisely in this vulnerable position, that you can ask God to open your heart to trust. You are standing in this position without a facade, without protection, without someone else's approval, and may even look a bit silly with your arms out to the sides. Know that you are infinitely loved by God, and that you are absolutely safe in God's presence no matter what. Be receptive of this.

MEDITATION

I INHALE AND BEGIN WITH...

MY HEART IS SAFE ◆ I TRUST THE LORD

I LIVE ◆ IN CHRIST

MAKE SLOW MOVEMENTS WITH DEEP BREATHS

Read 1 Corinthians 8: 6 NRSV

Yet for us there is one God, the Father, from whom are all things and for whom we exist, and one Lord, Jesus Christ, through whom are all things and through whom we exist.

Go outside or to a window and look outside. Let your eyes gaze at what you see - one thing at a time. If you see a tree, say slowly: 'The tree exists in Christ.' If you see a house, you say slowly: 'The house exists in Christ.' If you see the sky, say: 'The sky exists in Christ.'

Mention what you see, big and small, by name and meditate in this way that EVERYTHING really exists in Christ.

MEDITATION

INHALE AND BEGIN WITH...

I EXIST ◆ IN CHRIST

FAITH

'Do you believe in God a lot?'
I always become a bit speechless when people ask me this. On one hand, I probably believe in God a lot compared to many others. On the other hand, I think that my belief could be significantly greater. What to answer?
Sometimes I also hear people say, 'I cannot believe in God.' The reality is that we all believe in something or other whether we recognize it or not. Nobody really KNOWS what the meaning of life is. No one really KNOWS exactly what happens after death. And can anyone ACTUALLY prove whether God exists or not? The great questions in life require faith and are individually decided.

Our belief or faith can also change over time. My experience is that faith in God can be easy in some periods and difficult in other periods. But I know that the more times I have seen God's unexplainable intervention in the life of myself and others - be it little or big things - the deeper my faith becomes.

The challenge is that most people think that what is proven scientifically, is not a matter of faith. But certain things are. You cannot prove the rules behind math. The rules of math are something we commonly agree on to be proven and logical. This we choose to accept as true and meaningful. Another challenge is, many are not aware of what they believe. They just follow the crowd and never think about their beliefs until death or illness comes knocking at the door. Then questions like this show up...

Which beliefs or values do I lean on to get 'a good life?'
What have I brought with me from my family of origin and just 'automatically' believe in?
What would I like to believe in?

PRAYER

Lord, how can I lean my existence upon something I cannot see?

Some days it is easier to wrap myself up and turn away from the place that I call Your face. Remind me that faith is not a thing I own. It is a gentle turning outward and upward to You. Let faith grow in me as an echo of Your constant kindness.

YOUR FAITH ◆ HAS HEALED YOU

MAKE SLOW MOVEMENTS WITH DEEP BREATHS

Read Matthew 9: 20-22 NIRV

Just then a woman came up behind Jesus. She had a sickness that made her bleed. It had lasted for 12 years. She touched the edge of his clothes. She thought, 'I only need to touch his clothes. Then I will be healed.'
Jesus turned and saw her. 'Dear woman, don't give up hope,' he said. 'Your faith has healed you.' The woman was healed at that moment.

INTERLUDE

The word 'heal' in the Bible has the meaning of 'being saved, restored and liberated.' The woman believed in Jesus and she was healed, but it was more than that. She was also restored, saved and liberated.

Today I encourage you to do the same as that woman: lift your hands toward Jesus with faith. Notice that she does not speak to Jesus, she only wants to touch him. Get onto your feet and raise one or both hands up. Let this posture be an act of faith. Maybe with your hands lifted you want to pray out loud what it is from which you long for Jesus to heal, restore or liberate you or someone else.

When done, gather your hands in front of your chest and fold your fingers. As your fingers clasp each other, in faith say thank you to Jesus for listening to your prayer. Know that God has heard you. No prayer is too small or unimportant for God. Remember that just as your fingers are wrapped around each other, just that close is God to you.

Finish the prayer by drawing a cross with your hands in front of your chest. There is no right or wrong way to do this. It's your cross that symbolizes Jesus Christ in you.

MEDITATION

I INHALE AND BEGIN WITH...

YOUR FAITH ◆ HAS HEALED YOU

GOD'S KINGDOM IS NOT A MATTER OF TALK BUT OF POWER

MAKE CALM MOVEMENTS WITH DEEP BREATHS

Read 1 Corinthians 4: 20 NIV

For the kingdom of God is not a matter of talk but of power.

The sentence is written here to emphasize the difference between 'talk' and 'power.' Do you believe that God's power or spirit is more or bigger than what can be expressed in words? Maybe you have grown up in a church where faith was all about the preaching and the understanding of God's word.

Living in God's power, guided by the Holy Spirit is a big part of the Christian life. It's God's Spirit who reminds you of praying for someone if a name pops into your head. It's that power that gives us strength to tell others about Christ or to pray for sick people. It is that which guides us and encourages us to take a new step in faith even though we might be scared.

God or the Holy Spirit will never guide us to do something that is not biblical. I believe God speaks to us in more ways than we often realize, in small whispers of ideas, encouragement, and love if we are attuned to them.

Find a place to sit and try to quiet your mind. Take some big inhales and exhales. Be still and ask God to speak to you. Whatever pops up in your mind, pray for it. Don't get caught up on one subject only. Let God guide your prayer to whatever. Try this for a few minutes.

Then move on and ask God:

Is there anyone that you want me to do something nice for?

A name might pop up. It can be your spouse, neighbor or co-worker. Maybe an idea of what you could do pops up. The smallest thing can have the biggest impact. Maybe it's a text message or card with the words: 'Thank you for being in my life. You mean the world to me.' Maybe you feel like sharing a song on YouTube or a Bible verse. Personally, I have always found that people really are grateful for the encouragement. If possible send the text now or write what you feel led to do, down on paper. This way you won't forget it or be afraid to forget it as you meditate.

MEDITATION

I INHALE AND BEGIN WITH...

NOT A MATTER OF TALK ◆ BUT OF POWER

I BELIEVE ◆
HELP MY DOUBTS

MAKE SLOW MOVEMENTS
WITH DEEP BREATHS

Read Mark 9: 17-27 The Message

A man out of the crowd answered, 'Teacher, I brought my mute son, made speechless by a demon, to you. Whenever it seizes him, it throws him to the ground. He foams at the mouth, grinds his teeth, and goes stiff as a board. I told your disciples, hoping they could deliver him, but they couldn't.'
Jesus said, 'What a generation! No sense of God! How many times do I have to go over these things? How much longer do I have to put up with this?*** Bring the boy here.' They brought him. When the demon saw Jesus, it threw the boy into a seizure, causing him to writhe on the ground and foam at the mouth.
He asked the boy's father, 'How long has this been going on?'
'Ever since he was a little boy. Many times it pitches him into fire or the river to do away with him. If you can do anything, do it. Have a heart and help us!'
Jesus said, 'If? There are no 'ifs' among believers. Anything can happen.'
No sooner were the words out of his mouth than the father cried, 'Then I believe. Help me with my doubts!'
Seeing that the crowd was forming fast, Jesus gave the vile spirit its marching orders: 'Dumb and deaf spirit, I command you—Out of him, and stay out!' Screaming, and with much thrashing about, it left. The boy was pale as a corpse, so people started saying, 'He's dead.' But Jesus, taking his hand, raised him. The boy stood up.

***Note: It's important to hear Jesus' words here not just as angry words. Read the text and picture how Jesus might have spoken the words (and maybe also other words) in a different way, perhaps with a big sigh, sad about the unbelief. He knew that so much good could happen if only the people would believe in him and God's power.

INTERLUDE

Let the story sink into your soul. Close your eyes and picture yourself standing in the crowd of people around Jesus. You see everything going on. Picture how the father of the boy speaks to Jesus in desperation. He loves his boy but is at the end of his rope. Listen to Jesus as he cries out in despair because of the father's unbelief. But also picture how Jesus looks at the boy and the father with love and care in his eyes. Imagine how Jesus is not only interested in curing the boy but he also wants to teach the father something about faith.

Hear the father speak the honest words: 'I believe. Help me with my doubts!'

See how Jesus approaches the boy. Others are afraid to come close but not Jesus. Jesus drives out the demon that has been tormenting the boy. While the others believe the boy is dead, Jesus takes him by the hand and lifts him up in an act of love, trust and care for this boy.

This story is amazing in that it reminds us that faith in God does not have to be perfect or without doubt. It's not the 'amount' of faith we can pull together that heals. Jesus heals when we come to him honest about both our faith and doubt.

MEDITATION

I
INHALE AND BEGIN WITH...

I BELIEVE ◆ HELP MY DOUBTS

IF YOU ARE TIRED AND LONG FOR REST

My guess would be that 90% of the population would say that they are tired right now. They would confess to living in the 'fast lane' and would love to have an extra week of vacation if possible.

Today's pace is fast and we often have high expectations of ourselves and others, and what we are able to achieve. We feel bad or shameful because we can't live up to our own expectations and this only adds to our feelings of being tired and in need of rest. We might even quit praying and Bible reading because it's been too long since the last time, and it just becomes an extra thing we can't 'make right.'

The words of these meditations and devotions in this chapter remind us to let go. Remind yourself to release whatever you might be carrying around. Being with God is not just another thing on your 'to do' list. Being with God is rest, restoration and peace. Therefore let go of shame and a condemning conscience as you seek God today. Lay it down at the Cross. Let Christ be accountable for your day, your job, your family, your economy and your health. He will give you rest.

PRAYER

Father, I am tired, my thoughts are restless, my body is heavy. I need rest. Help me to let go for a while. You have given me this time to be a child. Help me fall into you who carry everything. Let me be a child, falling asleep on a forest floor.

COME TO ME ◆
I'LL GIVE YOU REST

MAKE SLOW MOVEMENTS
WITH DEEP BREATHS

Read Matthew 11: 28-30 The Message

'Are you tired? Worn out? Burned out on religion? Come to me. Get away with me and you'll recover your life. I'll show you how to take a real rest. Walk with me and work with me—watch how I do it. Learn the unforced rhythms of grace. I won't lay anything heavy or ill-fitting on you. Keep company with me and you'll learn to live freely and lightly.'

If we work too much or worry too much it tends to affect our shoulders. We tend to raise our shoulders a bit towards our ears. Doing this too much, we begin to feel pain in the upper back.
Try to roll your shoulders around a few times and notice how that feels.
As a symbol of 'letting go' try now to lift your shoulders as high up towards your ears as possible. Squish them up and hold them there as you count to 10. It's really uncomfortable. Let go of your shoulders with a big sigh. Repeat a few times.

Let this movement and the feeling of relaxation, after pulling your shoulders up, tell you something about letting go. Jesus is asking us to let go of it all and find real rest and recovery. Let your shoulders pray today: 'Jesus, help me. Help me learn the unforced rhythms of grace. I long to learn to live freely and lightly.'

MEDITATION

I INHALE AND BEGIN WITH...

COME TO ME ◆ I'LL GIVE YOU REST

BE STRONG ◆ HAVE HOPE

MAKE SLOW MOVEMENTS WITH DEEP BREATHS

Read Psalm 31: 23-25 NIV

In my alarm I said,
 'I am cut off from your sight!'

Yet you heard my cry for mercy
 when I called to you for help.

Love the Lord, all his faithful people!
The Lord preserves those who are true to him,
 but the proud he pays back in full.

Be strong and take heart,
all you who hope in the Lord.

INTERLUDE

Let the words 'be strong, have hope' be both a prayer and an encouragement from God today. Don't try to 'pull yourself together' today. Instead you are going to rest by laying down. Find an alarm clock and set the alarm for 5, 10 or 20 minutes if you have the opportunity. Remember, the alarm should not be too loud so that it startles you when it goes off.

Lay down on the floor, on your back, as comfortably as possible. If you can't remember today's meditation verse, place the book by your side.

Close your eyes and feel how you breathe slowly. Sigh out if you feel like it. When ready do a relaxing body 'scan.' You do this by giving attention to your head and face. Try to relax every muscle. Even open your mouth a bit, relaxing your jaw. Then let your attention move slowly over your shoulders, chest, arms, belly, and the rest of your body.

Hopefully after doing the body scan, you are all softened up and have no unwanted tension in your muscles.

Maybe then meditate on the verse: 'Be strong, have hope.' Lock hope in your heart. Or just stay down on the floor, letting go of 'to do' thoughts or worries as soon as they show up.

MEDITATION

INHALE AND BEGIN WITH...

BE STRONG ◆ HAVE HOPE

FOR GOD ◆ ALL THINGS ARE POSSIBLE

MAKE SLOW MOVEMENTS WITH DEEP BREATHS

Read Matthew 19. 23-26. NRSV

Then Jesus said to his disciples, 'Truly I tell you, it will be hard for a rich person to enter the kingdom of heaven. Again I tell you, it is easier for a camel to go through the eye of a needle than for someone who is rich to enter the kingdom of God.' When the disciples heard this, they were greatly astounded and said, 'Then who can be saved?' But Jesus looked at them and said, 'For mortals it is impossible, but for God all things are possible.'

God has no hard feelings against rich people. A lot of the people we hear about in the Old Testament were very rich and they were blessed by God. What we are reminded of in this text is that money and our salary can become too important in our lives. Money and possessions can seduce us.

'I have to work this much to make ends meet for me and my family.'

'I need to have this or say this not to seem weird or to be accepted.'

But do you really? What would really happen if you did not work as much, clean as much, get the stuff you feel is so important? Would you die? Would people really think less of you? Would you stop loving the people you really care about and would they stop loving you?

Please stop making excuses for your own choices. There is seldom anything 'you have to,' but there might be a lot of things you 'choose to.'

If you were to make big changes in your life, in order to find more rest, things would look different. That can be scary, but listen to the words today: 'For God, all things are possible.' (Matthew 19:26)

God can change hard circumstances. God can and will help you with hard choices.

If your problem finances are one reason why you are tired, then surrender your finances to God. Let go of the strange idea that you somehow are the only person in the world who can make ends meet. God knows your needs.

Come down on your knees. Perhaps like the picture on the cover of this book. Open your empty hands and give all that is holding you down to God. Mention each subject by name. Everything you worry about.

Finish by thanking God that all is possible!

MEDITATION

I

INHALE AND BEGIN WITH...

FOR GOD ◆ ALL THINGS ARE POSSIBLE

WHEN YOU EXPERIENCE FEAR OR WORRY

Fear and worry take away joy. Worries about the future, about children, the opinions of others, fear of what people say, all are known to most of us. We can ruminate obsessively without a sense of being able to stop. Fear paralyzes us and can cause us to make poor choices.

Fear and worry are some of the consequences of the error of Adam and Eve. That life is not the way God created it to be. God never gives us worry or fear, even though he never has said it would be easy. However he has promised us that he will be with us through it all. This is one of the reasons we have the Bible. Through faith in what God promises us in the Bible, he will walk with us and lift our burdens, in all situations.

The meditations and exercises in this section are tools to help clear the way for you through worry or fear. Every time you lose sight of what is ahead of you, breathe deeply and repeat your favorite words of meditation. Break the cycle of the fearful thoughts with words of hope, life and God's faithfulness.

PRAYER

Jesus, I can't let go of my worries,
but I don't want them to rule me.
Please meet me in my fears, carry them for me.
You who knew anxiety when Your world grew
dark. You chose to love, to reach out, to be in
connection with me.
Help me to look up and outwards too
when I am caught in my own darkness.
Help me to act when it is good to act,
and to let go when it is good to do so.
Help me to believe that I belong to You and
that I am safe in the face of the unknown.
Thank You for walking with me, for never
leaving me alone.

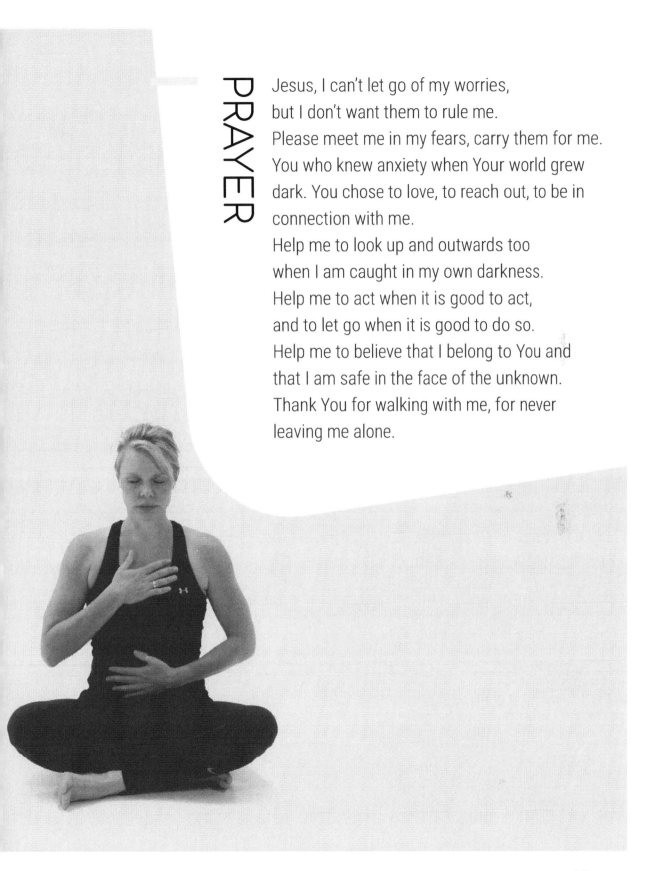

I AM ◆ A CHILD OF GOD

MAKE SLOW MOVEMENTS WITH DEEP BREATHS

Read Galatians 4:4-7 The Message

But when the time arrived that was set by God the Father, God sent his Son, born among us of a woman, born under the conditions of the law so that he might redeem those of us who have been kidnapped by the law. Thus we have been set free to experience our rightful heritage. You can tell for sure that you are now fully adopted as his own children because God sent the Spirit of his Son into our lives crying out, 'Papa! Father!' Doesn't that privilege of intimate conversation with God make it plain that you are not a slave, but a child? And if you are a child, you're also an heir, with complete access to the inheritance.

Close your eyes for a moment and visualize a child working hard on making a sand castle. You can picture how the child is trying over and over again to make the sand stick where it is supposed to. Now see how the gentle voice of the child's parent makes the child turn around. The voice is saying: 'Can I help you?' The child has a choice. It can keep going on its own, or the child can run to the parent and get help and advice, how to continue.

Picture yourself being this child. What would you do if the parent was God talking to you? Would you not turn around and run to God? Cast your worries away and run into the arms of God. Sense God smiling at you. Feel the safety of God's arms around you. God says: 'You are my child and I love you. I am here for you.'

Stay in this moment for as long as you like, then meditate on the words.

MEDITATION

INHALE AND BEGIN WITH...

I AM ◆ A CHILD OF GOD

I AM ◆ WORTHY

MAKE SLOW MOVEMENTS
WITH DEEP BREATHS

Read Luke 12: 22-25 NIV

Then Jesus said to his disciples: 'Therefore I tell you, do not worry about your life, what you will eat; or about your body, what you will wear. For life is more than food, and the body more than clothes. Consider the ravens: They do not sow or reap, they have no storeroom or barn; yet God feeds them. And how much more valuable you are than birds! Who of you by worrying can add a single hour to your life? Since you cannot do this very little thing, why do you worry about the rest?

If possible have a look at the Nature around you. Look at the birds, the trees. See how the wind catches the branches, notice the rhythm of the rain or the rays of the sun. Lift your eyes towards the sky, notice the clouds, or the deep blue color that stretches out into the universe.

God has created it all. God's eyes are on the birds, the spiders, the flowers. God's love creates and maintains Nature's flow of life. If God can do this, how much more can God see to your needs? God has time to listen to your worries, and loves being in contact with you - to hear you speak whatever is on your mind. You are full of worth in God's eyes. You are completely worthy.

MEDITATION

I INHALE AND BEGIN WITH...

I AM ◆ WORTHY

YOU SEARCH ME ◆
YOU KNOW ME

MAKE SLOW MOVEMENTS
WITH DEEP BREATHS

Read Psalm 139: 1-12 NIV

You have searched me, Lord,
and you know me.
You know when I sit and when I rise;
you perceive my thoughts from afar.
You discern my going out and my lying down;
you are familiar with all my ways.
Before a word is on my tongue
you, Lord, know it completely.
You hem me in behind and before,
and you lay your hand upon me.
Such knowledge is too wonderful for me,
too lofty for me to attain.
Where can I go from your Spirit?
Where can I flee from your presence?
If I go up to the heavens, you are there;
if I make my bed in the depths, you are there.
If I rise on the wings of the dawn,
if I settle on the far side of the sea,
even there your hand will guide me,
your right hand will hold me fast.
If I say, 'Surely the darkness will hide me
and the light become night around me,'
even the darkness will not be dark to you;
the night will shine like the day,
for darkness is as light to you.

To be known by God can be both terrifying and comforting at the same time. You cannot hide from God. God sees you when you feel ashamed, ugly and wrong, just as when you feel cheerful and well. There is no worry or shame that God does not know. Nothing is secret or too much for God. God even knows those things that are unknown to you. There is nothing you will have to walk through alone - not illness or suffering or even death. You are never alone.

God has gathered and kept all of your tears. God longs to comfort you. Let go of any fear of being known by God.

If you have a Bible, place it on your chest. (You can also use this book.) You can place your hands on top of it to hold it firmly on your chest. Let the book on your chest remind you that God sees you. God is as close to you as the book is. Thank God for knowing you. Surrender any worries you might have.

MEDITATION

I
INHALE AND BEGIN WITH...

YOU SEARCH ME ◆ YOU KNOW ME

WORSHIP GOD

In biblical terms, the word worship is equivalent to adore, to love, to look up to and to think highly of. Some might think of worship as the act of singing songs of worship, or hymns in church. Honestly, I believe we worship God just as much, or even more so, through our daily acts of love. Although songs of worship can be wonderful and uplifting, worship is more than merely singing to God.

The Bible tells us that there is nothing God desires more than our adoration. That we are to worship God with our whole being: body, mind and spirit. God longs to receive our worship expressed in our attitude, our daily choices, and the way we see people around us and act towards them. It is a lifestyle of putting God first. It is the mindset of knowing that we are forgiven, loved by God and called to love our neighbor as we love ourselves.

Worship songs and music, as well as the physical movements and meditations described in this devotion, are tools to help us focus on our daily worship of God. We tend to forget God so easily, in all the tasks of our daily lives.

PRAYER

Lord God who created all things,
You were broken to heal and restore.
You are like the great sea. I only see
a part of it, yet I get to swim in it.
Your being is so much greater, more
beautiful and more wonderful than I
can fathom.
I worship You for who You are and
surrender myself to You with body,
soul and spirit.

THE LORD IS GOOD ◆ GOD'S FAITHFULNESS ENDURES FOREVER

MAKE SLOW MOVEMENTS WITH DEEP BREATHS

Read Psalm 100 NIV

A psalm. For giving grateful praise.
Shout for joy to the Lord, all the earth.
Worship the Lord with gladness;
come before him with joyful songs.
Know that the Lord is God.
It is he who made us, and we are his;
we are his people, the sheep of his pasture.
Enter his gates with thanksgiving
and his courts with praise;
give thanks to him and praise his name.
For the Lord is good and his love endures forever;
his faithfulness continues through all generations.

What mood are you in at this moment? Sad, content, tired, disappointed, happy...?
No matter what mood you are in, try to worship God by just thanking God.
You don't have to be excited in order to worship, but you might get excited or experience a better mood through worship.

Thank God, not solely for what God is giving you, but just because God is the creator and sustainer of all that is good and loving. God is faithful, stable, and our protector as mentioned in the passage.

If you are by yourself, you might want to sing out loud or even shout out your praise and thanksgiving. You could say: 'Thank you God for your goodness. Your faithfulness endures forever. Thank you God for my family.'
Then continue in your own words.
You might feel awkward to shout out loud, but give it a try!

MEDITATION

INHALE AND BEGIN WITH...

THE LORD IS GOOD ◆ GOD'S FAITHFULNESS ENDURES FOREVER

TO GOD BE THE GLORY FOR ALL ETERNITY

MAKE SLOW MOVEMENTS WITH DEEP BREATHS

Read Romans 11: 33-36 NIV

Oh, the depth of the riches of the wisdom and knowledge of God!
How unsearchable his judgments,
and his paths beyond tracing out!
'Who has known the mind of the Lord?
Or who has been his counselor?'
'Who has ever given to God,
that God should repay them?'
For from him and through him and for him are all things.
To him be the glory forever! Amen.

Worship means that you acknowledge who God is and who you are. At times God might be thought of as a nice therapist or even Santa Claus, someone we can approach when in need.

We get upset and accuse God when things don't go our way. But there is nothing we can demand from God. 'If I behave well, I deserve what God will do for me.' But it doesn't work that way.

God is Lord.

God is always right.

God is always fair and just.

God is without beginning or end.

God is the fourth and the fifth dimension of existence.

God is omnipotent and so mind-blowing, an entity our brains really can't comprehend fully.

If possible look outside into the sky. Can you see the edge of the sky? Can you understand how great the sky above you is? 'For from him and through him and for him are all things. To him be the glory forever!'

MEDITATION

I

INHALE AND BEGIN WITH...

TO GOD BE THE GLORY ◆
FOR ALL ETERNITY

IN GOD ◆ ALL THINGS ARE CREATED

MAKE SLOW MOVEMENTS WITH DEEP BREATHS

Read Colossians 1: 13-17. NIV

For he has rescued us from the dominion of darkness and brought us into the kingdom of the Son he loves, in whom we have redemption, the forgiveness of sins.

The Son is the image of the invisible God, the firstborn over all creation. For in him all things were created: things in heaven and on earth, visible and invisible, whether thrones or powers or rulers or authorities; all things have been created through him and for him. He is before all things, and in him all things hold together.

Read the text slowly again. Try to 'taste' every word. It is a crazily amazing description of Jesus and his power.

With body and soul we worship God today. Find some gospel music or instrumental that you love. If you have no idea of what to play, you can go on YouTube and search 'Caleb and Kelsey - Worship (2018).' They sing slow worship music.

Bow down on your knees as pictured on the cover, or stand up with your arms out to your sides. You don't have to feel a certain way. You worship not because you 'feel like it,' but because God is worthy of all praise. Picture God on the throne as you worship with your whole body. Picture angels singing 'thank you praises' to God. Imagine the throne of God created with all the natural beauty in the world. Mountains, rivers, flowers, waterfalls, sunrises, stars. Picture God as the most beautiful being or entity you have ever seen. God is more amazing, greater and more loving that you can ever grasp with your mind.
Worship God for what and who God was, is and forever will be, for as long as you want. Let the beauty of God rub off on you... and saturate your being.

MEDITATION

I
INHALE AND BEGIN WITH...

IN GOD ◆ ALL THINGS ARE CREATED

WHEN YOU ARE FRUSTRATED

Emotions and perceptions that are difficult to contain and endure, tend to create frustration. We feel upset and get stressed and nervous all at once. Frustration will typically manifest itself by a growing feeling of unease which needs a physical outlet. At times it can be hard to find ways to rid ourselves of our frustrations and we can feel trapped by them.

It might be helpful to talk to someone, but it might also be relieving to physically let off steam. If you are frustrated, find solitude, and walk around. You might want to 'safely' let it out by punching a pillow or couch, kicking out in the air or at a ball, maybe even screaming out loud in a private place. You can try one of the more advanced sequences in this book and allow yourself to breathe hard, or moan and sigh loudly while moving. It is important not to hold back. Let go of your 'good' manners and 'proper' behavior when allowing your body to liberate itself from feelings of frustration.

Know that there is nothing to be ashamed of. God can contain your frustration and your outcry. We are the ones to hold back from God maybe due to shame. Pour out your frustration and let God fill you up. Take God's many promises and meditate on them.

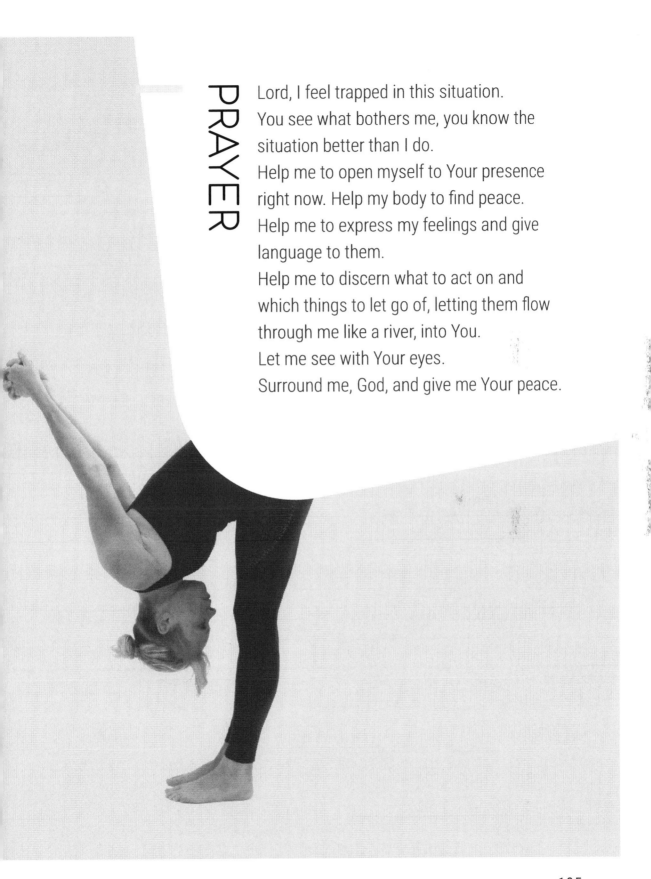

PRAYER

Lord, I feel trapped in this situation.
You see what bothers me, you know the situation better than I do.
Help me to open myself to Your presence right now. Help my body to find peace.
Help me to express my feelings and give language to them.
Help me to discern what to act on and which things to let go of, letting them flow through me like a river, into You.
Let me see with Your eyes.
Surround me, God, and give me Your peace.

NOT BY POWER ◆ BUT BY MY SPIRIT

MAKE SLOW MOVEMENTS WITH DEEP BREATHS

Read Zechariah 4: 6b NIV

Not by might, nor by power,
but by my spirit, says the Lord of hosts.

We can be strong minded. We can think that our intellect, our planning, our competencies or willpower makes all the difference in the world. The truth is that all this is good but it is not our own willpower that makes the world turn.

When we lose control and cannot plan our way out of everything, we get frustrated. Instead of trying to keep solving the problem with our own skills, contemplate and receive the words about God's Spirit.

Today as you sit down, let the Spirit of God be symbolized by your respiratory system. You breathe mostly without being aware of it. A guess is that we are unconscious of 99% of the inhales and exhales we take. I believe that no human would live without God giving life, without God's Spirit in our breath.

Notice your breath. Make it slow and calm. As you breathe remind yourself of how your respiratory system is given by God, and not something you can will to be there or not.

As you inhale, breathe in God's Spirit, and let God make the changes that might need to happen.

MEDITATION

INHALE AND BEGIN WITH...

NOT BY MY POWER ◆ BUT BY YOUR SPIRIT

GOD IS FAITHFUL
GOD WILL PROVIDE A
WAY OUT

Read 1 Corinthians 10:13 NIV

No temptation has overtaken you except what is common to humankind. And God is faithful; he will not let you be tempted beyond what you can bear. But when you are tempted, he will also provide a way out so that you can endure it.

Frustration can make it hard to believe that God cares for us. We might ask: 'If God really cares for me, how can God allow this to happen to me? Why is God not removing the source of my frustration?'

I don't know why God allows you to be frustrated. But I do believe that God knows your questions, and that God's desire is that you bring your frustrations directly to God. Yes, even to scream out to God! Get on your feet and cry out loud your questions and frustrations. Talk out loud to God. Yell at God if that is what you feel like doing. Talk as if God is right there with you. Let go of 'politeness' and allow yourself to be the child that you are to your heavenly Father, your supernatural Parent.
(If circumstances don't allow you to cry out loud, maybe write it down in bold letters.) When you are done, take some deep breaths. Let your body and mind find rest before you do postures or other free movements.

MAKE CALM MOVEMENTS WITH DEEP BREATHS

MEDITATION

INHALE AND BEGIN WITH...

GOD IS FAITHFUL ◆ GOD WILL PROVIDE A WAY OUT

The words in the meditation might be a promise that you need to hold on to during the day. When dark clouds surround you, repeat God's promise to you. Remind yourself that God is faithful.

MAY CHRIST DWELL IN MY HEART ◆

MAKE SLOW MOVEMENTS WITH DEEP BREATHS

Read Ephesians 3: 14-21 NIV

For this reason I kneel before the Father, from whom every family in heaven and on earth derives its name. I pray that out of his glorious riches he may strengthen you with power through his Spirit in your inner being, so that Christ may dwell in your hearts through faith. And I pray that you, being rooted and established in love, may have power, together with all the Lord's holy people, to grasp how wide and long and high and deep is the love of Christ, and to know this love that surpasses knowledge—that you may be filled to the measure of all the fullness of God.

Now to him who is able to do immeasurably more than all we ask or imagine, according to his power that is at work within us, to him be glory in the church and in Christ Jesus throughout all generations, forever and ever! Amen.

INTERLUDE

If you are frustrated and perhaps lack words of expression, it can be great to borrow others' words. Place yourself in a kneeling position in front of a chair. Find a pillow or blanket and tuck it under your knees as padding. Let your elbows rest on the seat and place the book on the seat as well. Open your palms towards heaven. Let the text become a prayer. After each sentence, pause before continuing.

For this reason I kneel before the Father from whom every family in heaven and on earth derives its name.
I pray that your glorious riches may strengthen me with power through your Spirit in my inner being.
I pray that Christ may dwell in my heart through faith.
I pray that I may be rooted and established in your love.
That I may have power, together with all the Lord's holy people, to grasp how wide and long and high and deep your love is.
May I know your love that surpasses knowledge—that I may be filled to the measure of all the fullness of God.
Thank you God that you are able to do immeasurably more than all I can ask or imagine, according to your power that is at work within me.
To you be glory in the church and in Christ Jesus throughout all generations, forever and ever!
Amen.

You might pray the prayer again and substitute 'I' with 'we' or 'they', 'she' or 'he.'

MEDITATION

I INHALE AND BEGIN WITH...

MAY CHRIST ◆ DWELL IN MY HEART

WHEN YOU WANT TO PRAY FOR OTHERS

Praying for friends and family is important. It's not difficult to pray for people if you have not done it before. We can get so absorbed in our own feelings that we forget that others can be having a hard time and are in need of our prayers.

The Bible tells us that prayer makes a difference. God listens and God acts on prayer and our prayer for others. Sometimes God says 'yes' to what we pray for, and at other times may be working in our hearts or on our character, when God answers 'no' or 'wait.'

Expect that God will answer your prayers. Expect that it sometimes takes time before you know the answer. Expect that God can intervene supernaturally in a situation, but also know that God doesn't always choose to do so.

PRAYER

Father, All-loving Parent, You know the people that I am thinking of.
You created them, You look at them with love and joy. Hold them in your hands.
Jesus, walk with these people that I cannot carry. Hold them close to Your heart, give them light, peace and courage.
Holy Spirit, pray for them with your ineffable sighs that they may have what they need.
I surrender these and their circumstances to You.

YOUR KINGDOM COME YOUR WILL BE DONE

MAKE SLOW MOVEMENTS WITH DEEP BREATHS

Read Matthew 6: 6-13 NIV

But when you pray, go into your room, close the door and pray to your Father, who is unseen. Then your Father, who sees what is done in secret, will reward you. And when you pray, do not keep on babbling like pagans, for they think they will be heard because of their many words. Do not be like them, for your Father knows what you need before you ask him.

This, then, is how you should pray:

Our Father in heaven,

hallowed be your name,

your kingdom come,

your will be done,

on earth as it is in heaven.

Give us today our daily bread.

And forgive us our debts,

as we also have forgiven our debtors.

And lead us not into temptation, but deliver us from the evil one.

For yours is the Kingdom and the power and the glory.

Amen.

INTERLUDE

Find something to write with and something to write on. Inspired by the text of the day we will not 'keep on babbling like pagans.' Instead you write names or topics on the paper. In the following, a list of topics are mentioned. Under each topic you write the names of the people, for whom you are praying. Writing down a name is your way of praying for them. Maybe you will write the same name several times. Use as much time as you like on each topic.

- Family
- Friends
- Work
- Church
- Your Country: Government, Health Care, etc.
- Our Planet and Nature

MEDITATION

I INHALE AND BEGIN WITH...

YOUR KINGDOM COME. ◆
YOUR WILL BE DONE

EVERYONE WHO ASKS, RECEIVES ◆ ANYONE WHO SEEKS, FINDS

MAKE SLOW MOVEMENTS WITH DEEP BREATHS

Read Matthew 7: 7-8 NIV

Ask and it will be given to you; seek and you will find; knock and the door will be opened to you. For everyone who asks receives; the one who seeks finds; and to the one who knocks, the door will be opened.

Today the prayer is oriented towards a topic. You may feel that some topics touch you more than others. This is only natural. Spend more time on the topics you feel resonate with your soul.

You are invited to use your body when you pray. This means you will place yourself in various postures, while you pray for the different topics mentioned below.

- For the sick, depressed and stressed in your own country and abroad. Sitting posture with your palms open and maybe hands resting on your thighs.
- For the seeking, e.g., those who seek God in emptiness, for satisfaction. Sit with your hands together in prayer posture in front of the heart.
- For the lonely. Stand with your hands crossed over your chest.
- For the poor in your country. Stand with your arms along the sides of your body and palms turned forward. Also called 'mountain pose.'
- For the persecuted Christians all over the world. Stand with your hands reaching out in front of you, elbows bent and close to the body. Palms turned upwards.
- For areas with war and chaos, and for those helping to create peace and reconciliation. On your knees in 'child pose,' palms turned upwards.

MEDITATION

I INHALE AND BEGIN WITH...

EVERYONE WHO ASKS, RECEIVES ◆ ANYONE WHO SEEKS, FINDS

WHEN YOU DON'T HAVE WORDS

We use so many words in the Church and in our Christian communities. Words help us understand ourselves and others, and last but not least, God. Words are good, but sometimes they are still insufficient when we try to express something. Maybe because we are not always able to put into words what we experience. Maybe because we cannot always understand what is going on in our heart of hearts. Sometimes, because words become worn out and somehow seem to lose their sense of meaning.

The calm and free yoga postures used in this book I consider 'wordless prayers.' With our breath, our body and movements, we intentionally and physically seek God and receive from God, forcing our mind and verbal part of the brain to take a 'back' seat in the process of prayer.

We all know how wonderful it can be to be silent and just be 'present' with people we feel safe with, even without speaking. Smiles, body language, and eye contact often communicate feelings more than words.

PRAYER

Holy Spirit, who lives in my breath,
weave Yourself through my darkness.
Rest on my tired thoughts like dew.
Pray within my heart,
I don't have the words...

SEARCH ◆ MY HEART

MAKE SLOW MOVEMENTS WITH DEEP BREATHS

Read Romans 8: 24-27 NIV

For in this hope we were saved. But hope that is seen is no hope at all. Who hopes for what they already have? But if we hope for what we do not yet have, we wait for it patiently.

In the same way, the Spirit helps us in our weakness. We do not know what we ought to pray for, but the Spirit himself intercedes for us through wordless groans. And he who searches our hearts knows the mind of the Spirit, because the Spirit intercedes for God's people in accordance with the will of God.

INTERLUDE

Sigh out loud. That means inhale through the nose and sigh out loudly through your mouth. Do this a few times but not to the extent that you get dizzy.

While you sigh, you can remind yourself that the Spirit intercedes for you with 'wordless groans' and searches the heart.

A sigh can be an expression of frustration and tiredness, as well as an expression of relaxation and a feeling of contentment. Let your sigh express exactly what you feel today.

MEDITATION

INHALE AND BEGIN WITH...

GOD, SEARCH ◆ MY HEART

JE ◆ SUS

MAKE SLOW MOVEMENTS
WITH DEEP BREATHS

The Jesus-prayer is a simple prayer from the Orthodox Church. The prayer is also called 'heart-prayer.'
It is said to originate from the 1300's. It is inspired by the blind beggar Bartimaeus' cry to Jesus: 'Jesus, Son of David, have mercy on me.'
(Mark 10: 47. NIV)

Prayer said in the rhythm of breath is the foundation of all the meditations in this book. The Jesus-prayer is a wonderful meditation when you don't have words, but desire to pray or meditate.

INTERLUDE

Let your body do the talking today. Sit down or stand up. Find a pose that makes sense to you. Maybe you just want to lay down and place your body in the shape of a cross, with your arms stretched out to each side.

In this open posture, use the meditation word for today: Jesus.

MEDITATION

I
INHALE AND BEGIN WITH...

JE ◆ SUS

You might use the longer version:

JESUS, SON OF DAVID ◆ HAVE MERCY ON ME

MAY GOD'S FULLNESS LIVE IN MY HEART

MAKE SLOW MOVEMENTS WITH DEEP BREATHS

Read Ephesians 3: 14-19 NIV

For this reason I kneel before the Father, from whom every family in heaven and on earth derives its name.

I pray that out of his glorious riches he may strengthen you with power through his Spirit in your inner being, so that Christ may dwell in your hearts through faith. And I pray that you, being rooted and established in love, may have power, together with all the Lord's holy people, to grasp how wide and long and high and deep is the love of Christ, and to know this love that surpasses knowledge—that you may be filled to the measure of all the fullness of God.

Find a comfortable sitting or standing position. Notice your breath and take deep inhales and exhales without getting dizzy. Place your palms together in front of your chest in prayer pose. As you inhale, release your hands out to each side of your body and make a big circle with your arms. Place your palms together again somewhere over your head. As you exhale, pull your hands down in front of your face and stop in prayer pose (at your chest.) Repeat the move as many times as you like, following the pace of your breath.

As you draw your arm circle in the air, picture the fullness of God being drawn into your heart. God's measure of fullness... just what you need today.

MEDITATION

INHALE AND BEGIN WITH...

MAY GOD'S FULLNESS ◆ LIVE IN MY HEART

IF YOU ARE SAD

When we are sorrowful or sad it can be a relief to cry. Humans are God's only creation that can cry. Animals can moisten their eyes with tears, but they don't cry. Jesus cried. He cried with sorrow, and he cried while feeling anxious and praying in Gethsemane, before he was arrested. Try imagining Jesus crying - maybe even sobbing with his nose running, his face distorted by tears.

Why did God create us in such a way that we can cry? Perhaps because there are in tears certain hormones and chemicals that release stress and lessen pain.

I believe that tears and crying are a gift from God to us. It is a release to cry and - especially in deep sobbing - to let go of all inhibitions. In deep sobbing we let go of control and propriety, and that's healthy. We let down our 'nice' facade when we dare to be vulnerable. The world doesn't need another Superman or Wonder Woman. The world needs people who dare to be vulnerable and honest when life hurts.

Are you sad? Then let your tears flow if you feel the need. Don't try to analyze or understand why. Let it happen. And know that God sees you and holds you in his arms. He is as present as every tear, and as constant as every morning. Be still in his presence and let the gift of tears soothe you.

PRAYER

God, here are my dry and my wet, living tears.
Here is my pain, and here is what caused it.
Be with me now, You who are already here.
Be the river that carries me, holding me up so
I won't drown.
Help me to acknowledge my sensitivity and fragility
with the same tenderness that You do.
Transform my mourning to dancing and shouting.
And when it is time, help me let those things go,
as the raging storm fades toward the calm.

GOD IS LOVE ◆

MAKE SLOW MOVEMENTS WITH DEEP BREATHS

Read 1 John 4: 7-10 NIV

Dear friends, let us love one another, for love comes from God. Everyone who loves has been born of God and knows God. Whoever does not love does not know God, because God is love. This is how God showed his love among us: He sent his one and only Son into the world that we might live through him. This is love: not that we loved God, but that he loved us and sent his Son as an atoning sacrifice* for our sins.

* 'atoning sacrifice' points to Jesus who died for our sins - a substitute victim.

Let your right hand hold onto your left hand. Imagine that your right hand is God's hand. Your left hand is yours. Let your hands 'speak' to one another. Your right hand is always loving and embracing in a respectful manner. Your left hand can do anything - receive the caresses from the right hand, make a fist and punch the right hand, or it can do all of these things one after the other.

You don't need to understand why you do what you do with your left hand. Close your eyes and let your body do the talking with God, through your hands. Sometimes our bodies know our needs better than our minds.

MEDITATION

I INHALE AND BEGIN WITH...

GOD IS ◆ LOVE

GOD'S GRACE ◆
IS SUFFICIENT

MAKE CALM MOVEMENTS
WITH DEEP BREATHS

Read 2 Corinthians 12: 9-10 NIV

But he said to me, 'My grace** is sufficient for you, for my power is made perfect in weakness.' Therefore I will boast all the more gladly about my weaknesses, so that Christ's power may rest on me. That is why, for Christ's sake, I delight in weaknesses, in insults, in hardships, in persecutions, in difficulties. For when I am weak, then I am strong.

** Grace means receiving without deserving it. God loves us and forgives us when we don't deserve it, even when we keep turning our backs on God.

INTERLUDE

Find a version of the song: 'You Are My Hiding Place.' I love the version made by Selah from 2007.
If you can't find it, pick another song that tells you about being weak, and all about God's Grace.

Sit down comfortably or find a posture that for you symbolizes helplessness.
Listen to the song and receive the words as you sit 'helpless.' It is alright to admit that you are weak. To admit that you can't understand either the cause or the resulting effect of a given situation you are in.
Don't let yourself fall into a 'pity party.' Remember that God is strong and you have a choice. You can either keep looking at and focusing on what you can't do, or look to God and focus on what God can do.

When the song is done, meditate on the words below.

MEDITATION

INHALE AND BEGIN WITH...

GOD'S GRACE ◆ IS SUFFICIENT

WHEN I AM WEAK ◆ YOU ARE STRONG

GOD IS MAKING ◆ EVERYTHING NEW!

MAKE CALM MOVEMENTS WITH DEEP BREATHS

Read Revelation 21:3-5 NIRV

I heard a loud voice from the throne. It said, 'Look! God now makes his home with the people. He will live with them. They will be his people. And God himself will be with them and be their God. He will wipe away every tear from their eyes. There will be no more death. And there will be no more sadness. There will be no more crying or pain. Things are no longer the way they used to be.'

He who was sitting on the throne said, 'I am making everything new!'

INTERLUDE

The text describes heaven as John (author of the Book of Revelation) visioned it in his culture and time. In the Church we don't talk that much about heaven and one can wonder why. Perhaps because we have heard that heaven is a place where the streets are paved with gold, and we will sing with the angels in eternity. This might not seem relevant to you or even interest or excite you.

But heaven will be awesome. The Bible describes heaven as the most fantastic place to be and that is why the authors of the Bible describe heaven as made in gold. They thought that was awesome.

Try to think of heaven as the place where loneliness and all that destroys our relations with others will be gone. Death and sickness will no longer exist. Love, celebration, joy and laughter to make your heart sing, will all be there. Just know that all the things you love the most will be there, and all the things you dislike or makes you feel sad will be gone. God will make all things new. What is broken today, will be healed there. What is sick, will be gone.

To picture heaven more concretely try to remember a place you have been that took your breath away with its beauty. Or a place where you felt safe, protected and peaceful. Close your eyes for a moment and let the memory fill your body, soul and mind. Imagine a heaven like that.

MEDITATION

INHALE AND BEGIN WITH...

GOD IS MAKING ◆ EVERYTHING NEW

GRATEFUL

Often it is a lot easier to complain than to be grateful or thankful. When the weather is cold we complain that it is too cold. When it is warm, well then, it is often 'way too hot.' Politicians are rarely talked about in the media when they succeed but often only when they fail or fall. In marriage it often can be significantly easier to see the downsides rather than the good sides of your spouse.

If you have two buckets standing in front of you and the one bucket symbolizes complaints and negative thinking, while the other symbolizes positive thinking and thankful thoughts, which bucket would then be filled the easiest?

We would do well to focus more on thankfulness and gratitude. What we fill our minds with, is also what will influence our everyday life. Awareness about what we can be thankful for - big things as well as small things - can help us have a more positive everyday life.

It is good to focus more on gratitude.

The positive influence of gratefulness is mentioned repeatedly in the Bible. Being grateful does something to us and for us. It makes us more capable of appreciating our faith and the gifts from God.

Being thankful reminds us that everything is given by God. Life, friends, Nature and the body are all gifts that we have been given. Let us avoid taking it all for granted and instead thank our Creator for these marvelous gifts.

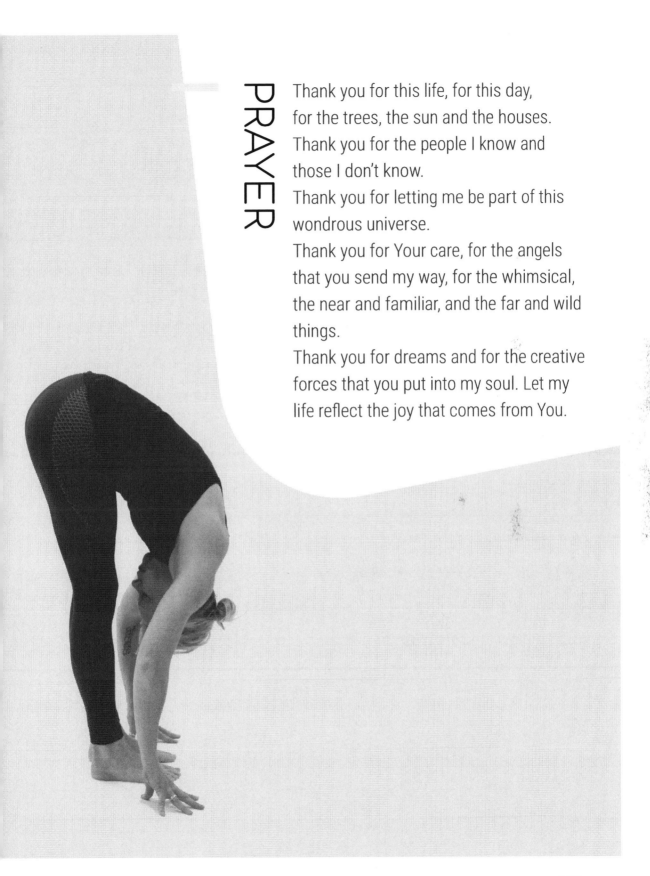

PRAYER

Thank you for this life, for this day,
for the trees, the sun and the houses.
Thank you for the people I know and
those I don't know.
Thank you for letting me be part of this
wondrous universe.
Thank you for Your care, for the angels
that you send my way, for the whimsical,
the near and familiar, and the far and wild
things.
Thank you for dreams and for the creative
forces that you put into my soul. Let my
life reflect the joy that comes from You.

GIVE THANKS ◆
IN ALL CIRCUMSTANCES

MAKE SLOW MOVEMENTS
WITH DEEP BREATH

Read 1 Thessalonians 5: 15-18 NIV

Make sure that nobody pays back wrong for wrong, but always strive to do what is good for each other and for everyone else.
Rejoice always, pray continually, give thanks in all circumstances; for this is God's will for you in Christ Jesus.

Look around you, or walk outside if possible. Let your gaze find something to look at and say thank you for what you see. Look at each detail, the shape, beauty or functionality. Give thanks to God for it all. Find at least 7 things for which you can give thanks. I would recommend next that you find one thing in particular. Pick it up and hold it. Place it somewhere where you are able to see it during your day. As you look at it, may it remind you to be grateful. Let it remind you that everything you have is a gift from God.

MEDITATION

I INHALE AND BEGIN WITH...

GIVE THANKS ◆ IN ALL CIRCUMSTANCES

I PRAISE YOU ◆ I AM WONDERFULLY MADE

MAKE SLOW MOVEMENTS WITH DEEP BREATHS

Read Psalm 139: 13-16 NIV

For you created my inmost being;
you knit me together in my mother's womb.
I praise you because I am fearfully and wonderfully made;
your works are wonderful,
I know that full well.
My frame was not hidden from you
when I was made in the secret place,
when I was woven together in the depths of the earth.
Your eyes saw my unformed body;
all the days ordained for me were written in your book
before one of them came to be.

Sit in a pleasant way so that you can see your feet and legs.

If you have a distinctly negative notion about your body, the following meditation can be difficult, but also very important. You might have to do the exercise many times before you can sense the gratitude.

Refrain from all criticism. Just say thanks for all that you have instead. God gave you your body and it is amazing.

Begin by looking at your feet. Thank God for your feet and where they have taken you. Then look at your legs. Thank God for your legs.

Look at your abdomen. Thank God for it, for your stomach and digestion, sexuality and all your inner organs, e.g., your heart that makes your body viable and functional. Give thanks for your breath.

Look at your hands and arms and say thanks for them. Say thanks for what they can give and do.

Feel your face with your hands. Thank God for what you feel with your hands.

MEDITATION

INHALE AND BEGIN WITH...

I THANK YOU ◆ I AM WONDERFULLY MADE

TO GOD THE FATHER THANKS FOR EVERYTHING

Read Ephesians 5: 15-20 NIV

See then that you walk circumspectly, not as fools but as wise, redeeming the time, because the days are evil.
Therefore do not be unwise, but understand what the will of the Lord is. And do not be drunk with wine, in which is dissipation; but be filled with the Spirit, speaking to one another in psalms and hymns and spiritual songs, singing and making melody in your heart to the Lord, giving thanks always for all things to God the Father in the name of our Lord Jesus Christ.

INTERLUDE

Put on your favourite music and start moving. Today you will be 'singing and making melody in your heart to the Lord, giving thanks always' (verse 20.) Use your body, use your voice and let your movements express your thanks to God.

If the thought appears: 'This is just too strange' - let it go. You are allowed to have fun and move your body in whatever way you like, as you say 'thanks.' God has given you the functionality of your body. Give thanks for it.

The reason we do not use our bodies that much in church services today is mainly due to cultural habits rather than biblical principle. Today don't hold back. Just let the body play its own song of gratitude to God.

Let your free movements be enough for today or continue making calm movements while taking deep breaths.

MEDITATION

INHALE AND BEGIN WITH...

GOD THE FATHER ◆ THANK YOU FOR EVERYTHING

Perhaps prolong the meditation with the following sentence:

JESUS CHRIST ◆ THANKS FOR EVERYTHING
HOLY SPIRIT ◆ THANKS FOR EVERYTHING

WHEN YOU LACK ENERGY AND COURAGE

To be muscular, fit and strong is in fashion these days. Strength is not something that comes to us in a magical way. Toned muscles require the heavy lifting of weights and a dedicated effort.

In Christian belief, strength is a strangely ambiguous thing. On the one hand, a strong belief is dependent on us being dedicated to Christ and seeking prayer, meditation, reading of the Bible and Christian fellowship. If we lose the influence of these things, our faith will get weak. On the other hand, a main message in Christianity is that we do not fight in our own strength or energy. God is, so to speak, our 'muscle' man. God's strength and courage does not come because we manage to 'pull ourselves together,' but because we throw ourselves into God's arms and mercy.

When we have no energy it is often easier to skip prayer and reading and just sit in front of the television and vegetate. To watch TV or a movie is not bad as such, but it cannot replace the nourishing of the soul. Your prayers do not have to be long, merely spend some time in the presence of God. For example, when you are hungry it is necessary for you to open your mouth and eat the food, if it is to give you energy. Food is the body's 'gasoline,' just like God's words and promises are spiritual gasoline for you when you lack energy and courage. Peacefully and quietly God will strengthen you and give you courage because of your trust in God.

PRAYER

Here I sit, empty of words and actions.

So much is trying to prevent me from doing what I want.

I don't want my circumstances to define me.

Help me to feel... my body, my skin, my pulse.

Be the blood in my veins. Let me rest in You, and when it is time, call me up and out. Give me Your lightness; let me sleep, eat and run like a deer in the meadows.

Help me not to demand anything of myself that You have not asked for.

Help me to listen to my life and see what is important today. Give me power and courage.

Let life come to me, day by day, with everything that I need.

BE STRONG ◆ IN GRACE

MAKE SLOW MOVEMENTS WITH DEEP BREATH

Read 2 Timothy 2: 1 NRSV

You then, my child, be strong in the grace that is in Christ Jesus.

INTERLUDE

Grace is a gift you receive and a condition that you are in. You never fall out of grace if you sin, as long as you turn back to God. If you believe in Christ, you have not fallen out of grace, even if you have not prayed for a long time. If you can't feel God's grace, remind yourself that your feelings are not always based on what is true in life. You can feel guilty or shameful without it being the reality in which God sees you.

I believe there is an evil entity on this earth. The Bible calls it the Devil or Satan. This evil entity has great enjoyment when he can convince God's children that they are not good enough, that they have fallen out of grace. But this is a lie. Therefore be strong in grace. This grace and your freedom were bought at the cost of Jesus' life.

If God's grace is hard to grasp maybe you need to make it more concrete. Take both your index fingers and poke yourself on the shoulders as you say out loud: 'I am...' Then, as you wrap your arms around yourself in front, say: '...in God's grace.' Repeat a few times until you feel like you can say it with certainty in your voice.

MEDITATION

I INHALE AND BEGIN WITH...

BE STRONG ◆ IN GRACE
Or meditate on the words you said earlier:
I AM ◆ IN GOD'S GRACE

THE LORD IS  _____

MAKE SLOW MOVEMENTS
WITH DEEP BREATH

Read Psalm 18: 1-2 NRSV

I love you, O Lord, my strength.
The Lord is my rock, my fortress, and my deliverer,
my God, my rock in whom I take refuge,
my shield, and the horn of my salvation, my stronghold.

INTERLUDE

King David, who wrote this psalm, uses many images for God's personality and qualities. Read through the list below where some of the image words are mentioned and try to 'chew on' each word. What does each word speak to you? What would it mean in your context? Is there anything these words have in common?

- Strength
- Rock
- Fortress
- Deliverer
- Refuge
- Shield
- Salvation

Is there another word that describes God better for you?

As you meditate today, pick one of the words on the list or another one of your choice.

MEDITATION

I INHALE AND BEGIN WITH...

THE LORD IS ◆ _____

I TAKE ON ◆ THE ARMOR OF GOD

MAKE SLOW MOVEMENTS WITH DEEP BREATH

Read Ephesians 6: 10-17 NRSV

Finally, be strong in the Lord and in the strength of his power. Put on the whole armor of God, so that you may be able to stand against the wiles of the devil. For our struggle is not against enemies of blood and flesh, but against the rulers, against the authorities, against the cosmic powers of this present darkness, against the spiritual forces of evil in the heavenly places. Therefore take up the whole armor of God, so that you may be able to withstand on that evil day, and having done everything, to stand firm. Stand therefore, and fasten the belt of truth around your waist, and put on the breastplate of righteousness. As shoes for your feet put on whatever will make you ready to proclaim the gospel of peace. With all of these, take the shield of faith, with which you will be able to quench all the flaming arrows of the evil one. Take the helmet of salvation, and the sword of the Spirit, which is the word of God.

The Christian path is also a path with spiritual struggles. In some churches spiritual battles are not something that people talk about. But for Jesus, and Paul who wrote the letter to the Ephesians, this evil is a reality. The spiritual battles most of us fight today might not be driving out demons as Jesus did. They might be the more hidden battles fought in our minds These can be negative thoughts about how one looks or ideas about yourself like: 'I'm never good enough, not clever enough, not strong enough,' and so on. It can be shame or blame. Thoughts that we repeat over and over in our mind, which destroy our joy in Christ and love for ourselves and the people around us.

Today we take up the armor of God and speak God's protection into our lives. So get up on your feet. Stand tall, with book in hand. We take on the armor piece by piece.

Stand firm Feel your feet on the floor placed hip-width apart so you stand firm. Then imagine that you put on 'shoes of readiness' to go and proclaim peace to the world around you. Pray for boldness to share God's peace, where others do not want to go.

Focus on your waist Fasten the 'belt of truth' around your waist. This is the ability to speak truth with love to all around you. Truth about yourself: You are a child of God. No one can take that away from you!

Focus on your chest and notice your breath Put on the 'breastplate of righteousness.' The world needs people who will fight for righteousness and speak up when unjust things happen. Remember that righteousness is not 'getting things your way' or 'getting even.'

Notice your left hand In your hand you are holding the 'shield of faith,' with which you will be able to quench all the 'flaming arrows' of the evil one. When shame and thoughts that discourage hit you, lift up the shield of faith. Remember the truth and what God thinks of you.

Focus on your right hand Pick up the 'sword of the Spirit,' which is the word of God. The Bible is full of promises you can use to fight against any strongholds that come your way. Pick it up and get ready to fight the battle.

And last, take on your head the 'helmet of salvation.' You are saved! You are standing in God's grace if you want to. Let this helmet protect your mind from wandering off into the wilderness of doubt, fear and anxiety.

MEDITATION

INHALE AND BEGIN WITH...

I TAKE ON ◆ THE ARMOR OF GOD

MOVEMENTS AND
ROUTINES

On the website www.crossyoga.org you can also download the routines as PDF files.

01 THE ROUTINE IS LIGHT

During this routine you stretch your lower back as well as your hip flexors. You will strengthen your back and buttocks. Your abdomen will also be strengthened if you 'suck in your navel' when you hold one leg and stretch the other. Each exercise can be repeated 8 to 20 times.

EXERCISE 1

EXERCISE 2

EXERCISE 3

EXERCISE 4

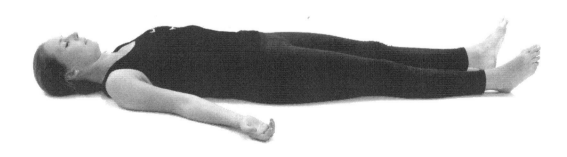

02 THE ROUTINE IS LIGHT

Part of this routine can be done while sitting on the floor, on a chair or standing if you are not comfort able sitting on the floor.

You will strengthen and stretch the muscles and tendons in the back of your neck, buttocks and back. Hold each pose as long as you like. This routine is not meant for repetition. Try aligning your breath with your movements. Repeat each exercise 10 to 20 times.

EXERCISE 1

EXERCISE 2

EXERCISE 3

EXERCISE 4
Hold the stretch and count slowly to 12.

EXERCISE 5

EXERCISE 6

03 THE ROUTINE IS LIGHT TO MEDIUM

This routine focuses on strengthening the back and shoulders. It includes bending backward, which is great, but you have to be careful if you have suffered from upper or lower back problems.

Repeat each exercise of the routine at least eight times. This however does not apply to the last two positions.

EXERCISE 1

EXERCISE 2

EXERCISE 3

Alternative:
on your knees

EXERCISE 4. Don't repeat.
Count to 10 as you hold it.

EXERCISE 5. Do not repeat.

04 THE ROUTINE IS LIGHT TO MEDIUM

In the routine you will strengthen your shoulders and thighs. You will also rotate your back and thereby stretch your lower back. You will stretch the backside of your legs in the forward bend, and you will use your back and abdomen, when you roll back up to your upright position at the end.
Repeat the routine as many times as you like.

REPEAT
THE ROUTINE

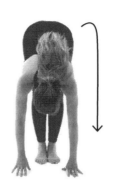

05 THE ROUTINE IS LIGHT TO MEDIUM

In this routine you bend and stretch your back and your hip flexors. Also, you stretch your shoulders and the backside of your legs and calves.
Repeat the routine as many times as you like.

REPEAT
THE ROUTINE

The front knee that is bent in the previous picture, is the one you stretch next.

06 THE ROUTINE IS MEDIUM

In this routine, you will be working most parts of your body. You will strengthen your legs, buttocks and balance. You will stretch your spine and lower back.

Repeat the routine an even number of times, in order to work both sides of your body equally.

REPEAT
THE ROUTINE

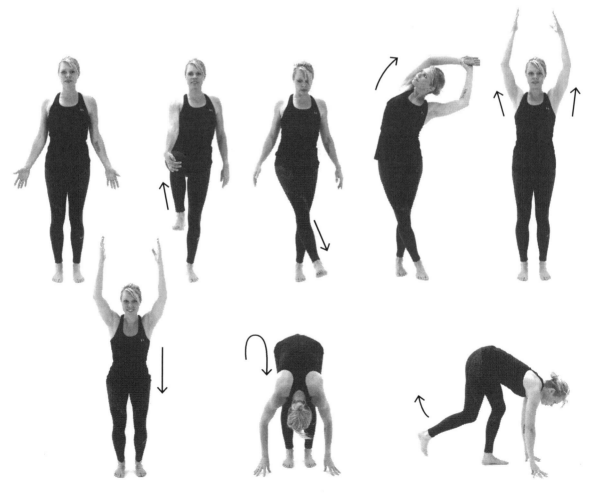

An easier option is to place your hand on your knee.

07 THE ROUTINE IS MEDIUM

In this routine you will strengthen your thighs, abdomen and shoulders. You will do forward and backward bends, and stretch the backside of your legs.
Repeat the routine on both sides as many times as you like.

REPEAT
THE ROUTINE

08 THE ROUTINE IS MEDIUM

In this routine you will do forward and backward bends. You will strengthen your shoulders, thighs and balance, as well as your abdominal muscles. Remember to change legs. The first time through the routine you move your right leg forward. The next time you repeat, you use your left leg.

Repeat the routine as many times as you like.

REPEAT THE ROUTINE

09 THE ROUTINE IS MEDIUM

In this routine you will strengthen your thighs, abdomen and shoulders. You will do forward and backward bends, and stretch the backside of your legs. Remember to change legs. The first time through the routine you move your right leg forward. The next time you repeat, you use your left leg.

Repeat the routine on both sides as many times as you like.

REPEAT THE ROUTINE

10 THE ROUTINE IS MEDIUM TO HARD

The routine contains many positions, which must be done standing and will strengthen your legs and buttocks. You will also strengthen your shoulders during the plank and the downward-facing dog. You will stretch your hips, the backside of your legs, as well as your back, in the different side stretches and forward bends. Remember to change legs. The first time through the routine you move your right leg forward. The next time you repeat, you use your left leg. Repeat the routine as many times as you like.

REPEAT
THE ROUTINE

11 THE ROUTINE IS MEDIUM TO HARD

In this routine you will strengthen your shoulders, arms, abdomen and buttocks. You will get some good stretches for your back, and train your balance.
Remember to change legs. The first time through the routine you move your right leg forward. The next time you repeat, you use your left leg.
Repeat the routine an even number of times, so that you practice your balance on both legs.

REPEAT
THE ROUTINE

Easier version
is on your knees.

12 THE ROUTINE IS MEDIUM TO HARD

This routine strengthens your balance and trains your legs and buttocks. You will open up your hips, and stretch your lower and upper back, as well as the backside of your legs.
Repeat the routine an even number of times to train your right and left sides equally.

REPEAT
THE ROUTINE

13 THE ROUTINE IS CHALLENGING

This routine strengthens your arms, abdomen, back and hips, as well as your balance. You will be stretching your calves, hip flexors, as well as rotating your spine, and stretching your lower back. Remember to change legs. The first time through the routine you move your right leg forward. The next time you repeat, you use your left leg.

REPEAT
THE ROUTINE

Photo: Dee Jones (Open Door Photography)

ABOUT THE AUTHOR
RIE FRILUND SKÅRHØJ

Rie is from Denmark and lives in Copenhagen with her husband and their three children.

Rie has a degree in Social Science from the University of Copenhagen and is the founder and leader of CrossYoga. (Christian yoga based in Europe)

Beside working with CrossYoga and teaching yoga in a studio, she is 'self-employed' and gives presentations and works as a consultant in 'Ledfrivillige.dk'. In English: Lead and manage volunteers. She has written two (Danish) books on the subject (in 2011 and 2014) and lots of articles in Danish NGO magazines.

Since 2010 Rie has been working 'part-time' as a fitness instructor, and in 2014 she began her journey with yoga. In 2015 she founded 'YogaFaith Denmark' which developed into CrossYoga in 2016.

CrossYoga is a network of Christian yoga instructors that offers classes in Europe. CrossYoga also 'organizes' yoga teacher trainings, retreats and workshops.

CrossYoga is offering both English and Danish yoga videos for free.
Find more information and links to free YouTube videos at:
 www.crossyoga.org

CrossYoga

BIBLIOGRAPHY

The Bible. Various translations.

Borgsø, Øyvind. **Bøn i bevægelse**. Areopagos 2015

Emerson, David. **Trauma-sensitive yoga in therapy**. Norton 2015

Keating, Thomas. **Åbent sind, åbent hjerte**. Boedal 2017

Kristen meditation. Div. forfattere. Sankt Ansgers Forlag 1999

Madsen, Ole Skjerbæk. **Christfulness - en udviklingsvej**. Areopagos 2017

Ryan, Thomas. **Prayer of heart & body**. Paulist Press1995

Ryan, Thomas (red). **Reclaiming the body in christian spirituality.** Paulist Press 2005

Thompson, Curt, M.D. **Anatomy of the soul** 2010

McCall, Timothy, M.D. **Yoga as medicine**. Bantram Dell 2007

Printed in Poland
by Amazon Fulfillment
Poland Sp. z o.o., Wrocław

52549433R00103